LOOK WHO'S MIXED UP WITH M*A*S*H THIS TIME!

DOÑA ANTOINETTA
Just this side of fifty, an ample-bosomed spinster, she had fallen from grace once in her life — with a man with a hairy chest and big, powerful arms — and confessed her sin in loving detail once a week to her long-suffering priest.

REVEREND MOTHER EMERITUS HOT LIPS
Head of the God Is Love In All Forms Christian Church, Inc., an organisation noted for its gay times (!). She wanted to make a gift to Doña Antoinetta — but what a gift!

WALTER WALDOWSKI
Doctor of Dental Surgery — the Painless Polack — he met his old buddies from M*A*S*H during an alcoholic binge in Paris, and hasn't been the same since!

BORIS KORSKY-RIMSAKOV
Some called him the World's Greatest Opera Singer. Others knew him as Old Lion Loins. He was a devoted practitioner of certain exercises said to improve his vocal performance, and that certainly endeared him to a vast numb

Other riotous M*A*S*H titles in Sphere books:

M*A*S*H Goes to Miami

**RICHARD HOOKER and
WILLIAM E. BUTTERWORTH**

SPHERE BOOKS LIMITED
30/32 Gray's Inn Road, London WC1X 8JL

First published in Great Britain by Sphere Books Ltd
1977
Copyright © Richard Hornberger and William E.
Butterworth 1976
Published by arrangement with the authors' agents

In fond memory of Malcolm Reiss, gentleman
literary agent
June 3, 1905 – December 17, 1975
   – Richard Hooker and W. E. Butterworth

Set in Photon Times

Printed in Great Britain by
C. Nicholls & Company Ltd
The Philips Park Press, Manchester

CHAPTER ONE

One of the many offices in various organisations held by Benjamin Franklin Pierce, M.D., F.A.C.S., chief of surgery of the Spruce Harbour, Maine, Medical Centre was that of official surgeon of Boy Scout Troop 147, of Spruce Harbour.

Normally, this was the least taxing and most pleasurable of his four appointments as surgeon to non-profit organisations. Dr. Pierce was also post surgeon, Rockbound Shores Post No. 5660, Veterans of Foreign Wars, Spruce Harbour; foundation surgeon, the Matthew Q. Framingham Foundation, Cambridge, Massachusetts; and Grand Exalted Royal Physician and Healer, Bayou Perdu Council, Knights of Columbus, Bayou Perdu, Louisiana.

Not by coincidence, in each post he had an assistant. Dr. John Francis Xavier McIntyre, F.A.C.S., his long-time friend and co-proprietor of Spruce Harbour's well-known Finest Kind Fish Market and Medical Clinic, also contributed (without charge) his professional services to the Boy Scouts, the V.F.W., the Framingham Foundation, and the K. of C.

Only the Boy Scouts, however, actually required any donation of professional services. Once a year, before starting out for summer camp, long lines of little boys appeared for physical examinations. Aside from that, and the occasional removal of a splinter or the diagnosis and treatment of poison ivy, the official surgical role of the two official surgeons had little to do with the practice of the healing arts.

For Post No. 5660 of the V.F.W., it was only necessary for one of the two healers to drop by the bar of the Post Home on Friday afternoon about five. This permitted the members of the post to truthfully tell their wives they would be a little late for supper as they were going 'to stop in and see the doctor.'

5

As foundation surgeon and deputy foundation surgeon, respectively, of the Matthew Q. Framingham Foundation, Pierce and McIntyre had even less to do. The foundation numbered sixty-two other properly licensed physicians in its membership. By a century-old tradition, the posts of foundation surgeon and deputy went to the last two physicians remaining on their feet at the annual Framingham Foundation Tribute to Hippocrates Banquet and Clambake. Their appointment was based on an ability having little to do with their knowledge of the practice of medicine.

Similarly, as Grand Exalted Royal Physician and Healer and Grand Exalted Royal Deputy Physician and Healer of Bayou Perdu Council, K. of C., they were never called upon to recommend so much as an aspirin. K. of C. rules and regulations required the appointment of duly licensed medical practitioners to the posts in each council, and the members of Bayou Perdu Council had no intention of appointing some spoilsport when Hawkeye* and Trapper John† were available.

As official surgeon and official deputy surgeon of Boy Scout Troop 147, however, it was clear to both Hawkeye and Trapper John that their firm duty under both the Boy Scout and Hippocratic oaths was to ensure that the scouts under their medical supervision were properly and adequately cared for while far from home and hearth at summer camp.

*Dr. Pierce's father was a devout fan of James Fenimore Cooper, and especially of his novel, *The Last of the Mohicans*. On the birth of his only child, he gave in to his wife, granting that 'Hawkeye' would appear a bit strange on a birth certificate. He had never, however, called his son anything else, and the name had stuck.

†Dr. McIntyre, while an undergraduate, succeeded in enticing a University of Maine coed into the gentleman's rest facility aboard a Boston & Maine railway train. When, made curious by certain obviously feminine murmurs of pleasure coming from that place, the conductor found them somewhat *deshabille*, the young lady traitorously announced that she had been 'trapped'. Dr. McIntyre has been known to friend and foe alike as Trapper John since that time.

On alternate days, therefore, either Hawkeye or Trapper John drove the thirty miles from Spruce Harbour to the summer camp, stopping for luncheon en route and arriving about one-fifteen, or just after lunch had been served to the Scouts. Neither healer was fond of *la cuisine* Boy Scout.

After ascertaining that none of their uniformed charges were suffering from anything more serious than a wasp sting or the first signs of acne, the next stop was the boat dock. As a privilege of their official position, they were free to make use of the fleet of Boy Scout boats. Furthermore, on a sort of roster basis, deserving Boy Scouts were granted the great privilege of wielding the oars. Lazy summer afternoons could thus be spent in piscatorial pleasure. If either physician had any luck, the rower could expect to have broiled fish for his evening meal, while his less fortunate fellows were forced to get by on the standard camp fare, which was frankly heavy on hot dogs and baked beans.

On one bright August afternoon, Dr. Pierce showed up at Camp Kitatinny with a stranger in tow. The camp chaplain, the Rev. Elmore T. Johnston, who had a very well-developed sniffer, was absolutely convinced that he smelled spirits on the stranger's breath, a suspicion buttressed somewhat by the telltale outline of a flask in the stranger's blue jeans.

The stranger was introduced as Horsey de la Chevaux, and when Mr. de la Chevaux acknowledged the introduction with a pronounced French accent, the Rev. Johnston felt quite sure that, for reasons he couldn't possibly understand, Dr. Pierce was in the company of a French-Canadian logger. The Maine woods abounded with French-Canadian loggers, most of whom were fond of the auce.

The Rev. Johnston erred slightly. He did indeed smell spiritous liquors on Mr. de la Chevaux's breath, and the bulge in the hip pocket of Mr. de la Chevaux's blue jeans was indeed a flask, but Mr. de la Chevaux was not a French-Canadian logger. He was, in fact, a Louisiana Cajun.

As Mr. de la Chevaux watched, Dr. Pierce removed two splinters, treated a nasty pimple, and painted with a patented medicine the nether regions of three young gentlemen who would, he said, remember in the future to look where they stood before they leaked, in order to avoid poison-ivy contamination of their nether regions.

And then, with two scouts in tow, Dr. Pierce and Mr, de la Chevaux proceeded to the boat dock. They settled themselves comfortably in the sterns of their respective row boats and were rowed to distant parts of the lake, where hooks were dropped into the water.

They had been fishing, without much success, for about thirty minutes when suddenly Mr. de la Chevaux called to Dr. Pierce.

'Hey, Hawkeye!' he called.

'Don't scare the fish!' Dr. Pierce hissed in reply.

'Take a look at the dock, Doc,' Mr. de la Chevaux went on.

There were three people on the dock – the Rev. Johnston and two Boy Scouts. Rev. Johnston was waving his arms around and one of the Boy Scouts was making signals with his arms.

'I hope,' Hawkeye said, 'that those are manifestations of religious fervor, and that the reverend hasn't been at the sauce again.'

'I tink,' Mr, de la Chevaux said, 'dat it's something serious, Hawkeye.'

Hawkeye looked again.

'He's signalling S.O.S.,' his Boy Scout rower said.

'In that case, pal,' Hawkeye said, 'you get up here and navigate, and I'll row.'

It was indeed an emergency of a medical nature.

'One of the boys has been badly cut,' Rev. Johnston said, even as Hawkeye was getting out of the row boat.

'How?' Hawkeye asked.

'The head came off an axe,' Rev. Johnston said.

'Where is he?'

'In the dispensary.'

'Get my bag, Horsey, will you?' Hawkeye called as Mr. de

8

la Chevaux pulled up to the dock in his row boat. 'One of the kids has been cut.'

The injured boy, black-haired, light brown in colour, was in pain, frightened, and on the edge of hysteria. That was understandable. He had been badly cut, and there was a good deal of blood. The cutting edge of the axe blade had opened his lower right arm to the bone. Hawkeye saw that the arm was broken as well. It was a nasty wound.

The camp director had applied a tourniquet. As Hawkeye waited for the bag from his car, he tried to speak to the boy. The boy looked at him uncomprehendingly.

'He doesn't speak much English, Doctor,' the camp director said, so shocked by the sight of the arm that he used Hawkeye's official title.

'How come?'

'He's Cuban,' the camp director said.

'Here you go,' Frenchy said, delivering the bag. And then he saw the boy. 'My God!'

'He doesn't speak any English, Frenchy,' Hawkeye said. 'Tell him that I'm a doctor, and that he's going to be all right.'

Frenchy, in what sounded like (and indeed was) fluent Spanish, spoke consolingly to the boy as Hawkeye applied a pressure compress to the wound.

'Get on the telephone,' Hawkeye said, 'and call the hospital and the state cops. Tell them to set up an operating room, and ask Dr. McIntyre and Nurse Flanagan to stand by. Tell the cops I'd appreciate an escort.'

The camp director reached for the telephone.

'Tell him, Frenchy,' Hawkeye said, 'that we're going to take him to the hospital and fix him up.'

Horsey did as he was told. The look of near animal terror in the boy's eyes seemed to diminish a little.

'You drive, Horsey,' Hawkeye said. 'We'll prop him up on the back seat, and I'll ride with him.'

A state police car was waiting at the intersection of the dirt road leading to Camp Kitatinny and the highway. As

Horsey eased the car onto the concrete, the siren began to wail.

Trapper John and Nurse Flanagan, a cart, two orderlies, and the emergency room intern were waiting for them when Horsey pulled up outside the Spruce Habour Medical Centre.

'Prep him,' Hawkeye said as the orderlies took the boy from the car. 'He doesn't speak much English, so Horsey will translate for you.'

Forty-five minutes later it was all over, and Hawkeye and Trapper John and Horsey, all three in surgical greens, stood around the small pale figure in the recovery room waiting for him to wake up.

'Where did he come from?' Trapper John asked. 'We don't have any Cubans around here.'

'The kid who was rowing me said that the troop had two of them up from Miami,' Hawkeye reported. 'Some sort of an exchange programme. I don't know where the other one was.'

'He was probably on the other end of the axe,' Trapper replied.

The small, greyish-faced figure stirred.

'Talk to him, Horsey,' Hawkeye ordered. 'Try to get his attention.'

After first throwing up all over Horsey's shoes, the boy woke up to find his arm in a cast. Thirty minutes after that, he was ready to leave the recovery room.

'Where do we put him?' Nurse Flanagan asked.

'Put him in with somebody cheerful,' Hawkeye ordered. 'Horsey and I will look in on him after a bit.'

Dr. Pierce, Dr. McIntyre, Nurse Flanagan and Col. de la Chevaux* then moved to Dr. Pierce's chief of surgery's

*Several years before, as has been recorded in *M*A*S*H Goes to New Orleans*, a volume already widely acclaimed for its literary style, attractive cover, stout binding, and remarkably low cost, Jean-Pierre de la Chevaux had been directly commissioned colonel in the Louisiana National Guard by His Excellency the Governor. Citing Mr. de la Chevaux's distinguished active military service record and his many civic good works, the governor stated that he was simply recognizing talent when he saw it. He 'refused to

10

office. The door was locked, the IN CONFERENCE sign in the anteroom illuminated, and the lower file drawer unlocked. From this stout steel repository were taken a bottle of gin, a bottle of vermouth, a jar of olives, suitable mixing utensils, and, for Col. de la Chevaux, who thought martinis were 'sissy', a half-gallon bottle of Old White Stagg Blended Kentucky Bourbon.

Within two minutes of entering the office, the three practitioners of the healing arts and the distinguished military representative of the Louisiana governor's staff were all sitting around the coffee table, feet up, having a wee nip.

'He gonna be all right, Hawkeye?' Horsey asked.

'He came close to a lot of trouble, but he'll be all right,' Dr. Pierce replied.

'He's a Cuban refugee,' Horsey said. 'They just sneaked him out of there.' He paused thoughtfully, and then grabbed the telephone on the coffee table.

Doctors Pierce and McIntyre and Nurse Flanagan each raised an eyebrow. They wondered what Horsey was doing, but none of them would ask. Hawkeye reached over and punched the button that turned on a loudspeaker, permitting them all to hear.

'Hey, Sweetie,' Horsey said to the hospital telephone operator. 'Lemme speak to Crumbum.'

'Is that you, Horsey?' the operator asked, nearly in a giggle.

'Who else?' Horsey replied.

'Thank you for the gumbo, Horsey,' the operator said.

'Glad you liked it,' Horsey said, blushing a little. 'We

---

dignify with a reply' allegations made by his political opponents that Col. de la Chevaux's appointment had come shortly after the discovery of 'the largest pool of natural gas ever found in North America' under de la Chevaux's property in Bayou Perdu, La., and that the appointment itself had been made at four o'clock in the morning in the bar at Brennan's Restaurant in New Orleans following what the New Orleans *Picaroon-Statesman* had editorially described as a 'booze-washed bacchanal setting new standards even for our governor.'

made a couple of pots for a party, but the Knights* started to drink a little early, and there was a lot left over, so I figured what the hell, I bring some with me. Hate to see it go to waste.'

'I'll connect you with Crumbum,' she said. Mr. T. Alfred Crumley served as administrator of the Spruce Harbour Medical Centre.

'T. Alfred Crumley speaking.' The voice was dignified, precise, and a trifle nasal.

'Hey, Crumbum,' Horsey said. 'Here's Horsey, how dey hanging?'

'Col. de la Chevaux,' Mr. Crumley said. 'As I have *told* you and *told* you, my name is Crum*ley*.'

'Right,' Horsey said. 'Hey, Crumbum, I want you to do something for me.'

'What?' Mr. Crumley asked, profound suspicion in his voice.

'Dere's a little kid in here, got cut with an axe. Name is Juan Francisco. Hawkeye, Trapper, and Esther just sewed him up.'

'I'm familiar with the case, Colonel,' T. Alfred Crumley replied.

'Give him whatever he needs,' Horsey de la Chevaux said. 'And put it on my tab.'

'That's very kind of you, Colonel,' T. Alfred Crumley said.

'Ah,' Horsey said, visibly embarrassed, 'he's a refugee from Cuba. He needs a little helping hand.' He changed the subject. 'Hey, Crumbum,' he said, 'There's a fifty-gallon barrel of gumbo in the kitchen.'

'I know,' T. Alfred Crumley said. 'I . . . caught a whiff of it as I came in the building.'

'Help yourself,' Horsey offered. 'Good for what ails you.'

'That's very kind of you, Colonel, I'm sure,' T. Alfred Crumley replied without much enthusiasm.

---

*Col. de la Chevaux referred to the Knights of the Bayou Perdu Council, Knights of Columbus, in which organisation he had for many years served as Grand Exalted Royal Keeper of the Golden Fleece, or treasurer.

'Forget it,' Horsey said grandly, and he hung up the phone. He reached for the half-gallon bottle of Old White Stagg, looped his index finger in the glass circle at the neck, and drank deeply. Then he stood up.

'Well, I hate to leave good company,' he said, 'but I got to go. I'll look in on the kid and take off.'

'Whither bound, Horsey?' Trapper John inquired.

'First to the North Slope of Alaska, and then to Borney,' Horsey replied. 'I promised the boys I'd bring them some gumbo.'

'Let me finish my drink,' Hawkeye said, 'and I'll look in on the kid with you.'

'Why not?' Horsey said. 'As Hot Lips always says, two belts is safer than one.'

He raised the half-gallon jug again, in the interests of safety, and then he and Dr. Pierce left the office.

Juan Francisco was twelve years old, and the young body heals remarkably quickly. The next morning Juan Francisco was walking around his room, and by the next afternoon, his cast colourfully decorated with Merthiolate drawings, was inquiring in broken English when he might be permitted to return to camp.

While Hawkeye didn't forget Juan (they in fact became buddies in the four days Juan was in the hospital), he didn't think much about him. What could have been a really bad business had turned out well, even so far as the depressing matter of paying the hospital tab was concerned. Even T. Alfred Crumley, that extraordinary worrier, placed absolute faith in Horsey de la Chevaux's credit.

When it was time for Juan to leave camp and return to Miami, Hawkeye prepared two envelopes. One, addressed to 'The Physician Concerned', contained a report of Juan's injuries, the treatments thereof, X-rays of the broken bones, and Hawkeye's recommendations on removal of the cast and physical therapy. The second contained photographs taken by Juan of the friends he had made among the hospital staff. At the last moment, Hawkeye paper-clipped a twenty-dollar bill to the bottom of the letter, and penned in a note saying it was to be used to go to Howard Johnson's in Miami to eat fried clams and remember his friends in Maine.

Then, with other business to attend to, the episode with Juan was filed in the back of his mind. It had been simply a pleasurable experience in the practice of medicine.

Hawkeye was, then, greatly surprised to receive, ten days later, a telephone call from the Honorable T. Bascomb ('Moosenose') Bartlett, mayor of Spruce Harbour, informing him that a delegation of Cuban-Americans was in his office. Would Hawkeye please come right down?

'Not just now, Moosenose,' Hawkeye replied. 'Thank you just the same.'

'I thought you'd react that way, Hawkeye,' Moosenose said. 'Your trouble is you have no civic pride.'

Hawkeye thought it was just a tart but idle comment, but like so many of his fellow Americans, he underestimated the depths to which politicians will sink to get their way.

He had barely had time to hang up the telephone when the door burst open and in stepped Jerome P. McGrory, attorney-at-law and public relations director of the Greater Spruce Harbour Chamber of Commerce.

'You've got the wrong place, Mac,' Hawkeye said. 'The ambulance chaser's door is at the rear.'

'This is for your own good, Hawkeye,' Mr. McGrory said, signalling with his hand. Two of Spruce Harbour's finest came in the door.

'There are two ways we can do this, Hawkeye,' McGrory said. 'You either come along peacefully and co-operate . . .'

'Or . . .'

'These gentlemen will carry you,' McGrory said. 'Think of it as a sacrifice you're making for the good of the community.'

'Think of *what* as a sacrifice?'

'All you have to do is go to Moosenose's office and accept a plaque from the Cubans.'

14

'What kind of a plaque?'

'For your selfless, patriotic, generous contribution to Cuban refugees, namely one Juan Francisco.'

'You're out of your gourd, shyster,' Hawkeye said conversationally.

'The television cameras are there,' McGrory went on, ignoring him. 'And representatives of the printed media. All you have to do, Hawkeye, is say "thank you." If you wanted to be a good guy and a responsible citizen with the best interests of your community at heart, you could even smile.'

'I'll sic Trapper John on you, McGrory,' Hawkeye said.

'Dr. McIntyre is at this very moment in His Honour the Mayor's office, waiting for you to show up,' McGrory said. 'He even brought his Polaroid camera.'

'For twenty years I have been nursing an Irish viper at my breast,' Hawkeye said. 'All right, McGrory, I know when I'm whipped. Lead on.'

CHAPTER TWO

Five minutes later, to a round of applause, Hawkeye entered the office of His Honour the Mayor, Moosenose Bartlett. The mayor was wearing his full dress morning suit, across the starched white bosom of which, in case there might be a question of his function, was stretched a purple ribbon with MAYOR lettered upon it in gold tinfoil.

There were also three strangers – a long thin one, a short fat one, and a middle-sized one as bald as a cue ball. They were chattering excitedly amongst themselves in Spanish, but stopped immediately when Hawkeye entered the room. Now they beamed at him.

'Any time you're ready, Moosenose,' a man standing behind a television camera said.

Moosenose, top hat square on his head, turned and beamed at the camera.

'Hello, out there in TV-land,' he said. 'This is your friend, the Honourable Moose ... T. Bascomb Bartlett, fifth-term mayor of our fair city of Spruce Harbour. This is a proud day for all of us. We have right here in our office three gentlemen who have come all the way from Miami, Florida, to pay tribute to one of the fine physicians of the Spruce Harbour Medical Centre.' He gestured to the three strangers. They joined him, somewhat nervously, in front of the camera. So did Jerome P. McGrory.

Moosenose, frankly, looked a little miffed, but he rose to the occasion.

'And this, of course, well known to all of you, is that distinguished attorney-at-law, Jerome P. McGrory, public relations director of the Spruce Harbour Chamber of Commerce, who only two days ago announced that he would, in the public interest, *abandon* his thriving practice of law for public service. He is seeking the office of district attorney.'

16

Jerome P. McGrory put his hands over his head, joined, in the manner of a winning prize-fighter.

'Come up here, Hawkeye,' His Honour the Mayor said. If it appeared to the television viewers that Dr. Pierce was being pushed before the cameras, he was.

He turned and glowered at someone off camera and then faced His Honour the Mayor.

'This is our own Dr. B. F. Pierce,' Moosenose said, 'and, I am proud to say, my lifelong friend.' Dr. Pierce looked a little ill.

'Unfortunately,' Moosenose went on, 'we were so pressed for time before this spontaneous broadcast that I didn't get these gentlemen's names. It doesn't really matter – they can't speak English anyway.'

The three Cuban gentlemen were beaming at Dr. Pierce. His Honour the Mayor snatched a shield-like plaque from the hands of the short fat one.

'I will read it to you,' Moosenose said, and proceeded to do so. ' "Presented to Dr. B. F. Pierce by the Cuban Refugee Association as a small tribute to his nobility in the practice of his profession." '

Hawkeye looked positively ill.

His Honour thrust the plaque at him, catching him by surprise.

'There you are, Dr. Pierce,' Moosenose said. 'Now, my lifelong friend, isn't there something you'd like to say to all the people out there in TV-land?'

Trapper John sat up. It was his considered judgment, based on his medical experience and long association with Hawkeye, that one of two things was going to happen. Hawkeye was either going to be physically ill (with a little luck, he thought, all over Moosenose's MAYOR sash), or he was going to punch Moosenose in the nose. Moosenose was called Moosenose because his nostrils were flat and exposed. The major reason they were flat and exposed was that Hawkeye Pierce had, from the age of five, found it necessary to regularly punch his lifelong friend in the snoot.

Whichever actually transpired, it would be long remem-

17

bered out there in TV-land, and Trapper John was determined to have it captured on film. He raised his camera to his eye. He was somewhat surprised to see Hawkeye smiling.

'Ladies and gentlemen,' Hawkeye said quite smoothly, 'I don't really know how to respond to all this.'

There was a pregnant pause. 'I don't really feel I can accept this,' Hawkeye went on. 'The word "nobility" has been mentioned. I have been a Boy Scout, a physician, an honorary member of the Knights of Columbus, a member of the Veterans of Foreign Wars, and a Classroom Daddy for the fifth grade at Spruce Harbour Elementary School. But I have only done one noble thing in my life, and treating Juan Francisco wasn't it.'

His Honour the Mayor looked as if he had been struck with deep emotion.

'Dr. Pierce,' he said, 'Hawkeye ... would you tell us all, your old friends and admirers, these foreigners from Miami, Florida, and all the folks out there in TV-land what that was?'

'What what was?'

'The one noble thing you did in your life?'

'Certainly,' Hawkeye said. He beamed at His Honour the Mayor, Political Hopeful McGrory, and all the folks out there in TV-land. 'One time I got to cheat a politician.'

While the languages are far from identical, there is enough similarity between Italian and Spanish to permit a certain level of communication. With this in mind, Hawkeye took the short fat Cuban by the arm and led him out of His Honour the Mayor's office, even before the political personage could manage to close his mouth, in search of one Wrong Way Napolitano. Mr. Napolitano was the proprietor of the Spruce Harbour International Airport,* and of Italian descent.

*Before a chartered DC-3 bound from Boston to Montreal had become lost and been forced to land at the facility for fuel, it was known as the Napolitano Truck Farm & Crop-Dusting Service. The change of name was the inspiration of the Spruce Harbour Chamber of Commerce.

The other Cuban gentlemen tagged along, as, of course, did Trapper John. He hadn't gotten the photograph he had hoped for of Hawkeye punching His Honour, but the mayor's face after Hawkeye's remarks had been a perfectly satisfactory substitute.

Within ten minutes, they were sitting around one of the wooden tables at the Bide-a-While Pool Hall/Ladies Served Fresh Lobsters & Clams Daily Restaurant and Saloon, Inc. Mr. Napolitano functioned as interpreter while the proprietor of the establishment, Stanley K. Warczinski, Sr., and his good lady brought pitchers of beer and trays of steaming lobsters to the table.

It came out that the Cuban gentlemen had a dual purpose in coming to Spruce Harbour. One of the reasons they were grateful to Hawkeye was that there had been no question of payment at the hospital. Juan Francisco had been treated and released and the question of money hadn't even come up.

'Tell them not to worry about it,' Hawkeye said. 'It's been taken care of.'

The short fat Cuban gentleman listened intently as the message was roughly translated. Something, Hawkeye and Trapper John saw, had gone wrong during the translation. People who are told that hospital bills are taken care of do not normally get red in the face, smack their foreheads with the palms of their hands, and otherwise act as if someone had questioned the marital status of their grandparents.

The short fat gentleman stood up, dipped into his pocket, and with some difficulty came out with a roll of one-hundred-dollar bills large enough to choke the proverbial horse.

One by one, he tossed them onto the table, meanwhile keeping up a steady exchange with his two friends.

'What's he say?' Hawkeye asked.

'He says just tell him how much,' Wrong Way answered, staring bug-eyed at the growing pile of bills.

'Enough is enough,' Hawkeye said.

'Ha!' the short fat Cuban gentleman said, glowering at him.

Finally, however, he ran out of money. He pointed indignantly at the tall thin Cuban gentleman, who rose, extracted a Moroccan leather wallet from his suitcoat breast pocket, and began to peel even more one-hundred-dollar notes from it. They fluttered down onto the growing pile on the table.

Hawkeye and Trapper John watched now in silent fascination until his supply of money was exhausted. The tall thin Cuban gentleman looked at Hawkeye, snorted, said, 'Ha!' and sat down. The middle-sized one now stood up. Instead of money, he threw a thick bundle of traveller's cheques onto the table. They were in the denomination of five hundred dollars.

Then all three of the Cubans sat back and looked expectantly at them.

Hawkeye carefully gathered the money together in a pile, laid the stack of traveller's cheques on top, and pushed it back toward them. Acting as one man, they pushed in the other direction.

'Wrong Way,' Hawkeye said, 'tell them that Horsey *paid the bill*. Tell them about Horsey.'

'How can you explain Horsey to anybody?' Wrong Way asked, quite reasonably.

'*Try*, Wrong Way,' Trapper John ordered.

Wrong Way's efforts, while valiant, were not very successful.

At this point, Esther Flanagan, R.N., unquestioned ruler of the Spruce Harbour Medical Centre's surgical wing, entered the establishment.

'This is a fine thing,' she said indignantly. 'There I am, waiting around for you guys in the office, and here you are, in the flushest poker game I've seen in years.' She looked around the table, fished under the money, and then inquired, 'Where're the cards?'

'What did she say?' the short fat Cuban gentleman asked in Spanish.

20

'I asked where the cards are,' Esther Flanagan replied, in Spanish.

'Flanagan, where did you learn how to speak Spanish?' Hawkeye asked.

'I did two tours at the naval hospital in Guantanamo Bay, Cuba,' Lt. Cmdr. E. Flanagan, U.S.N., Retired, replied. 'How else did you think I was translating for Juan Francisco?'

'You know Juan Francisco?' the short fat Cuban asked, still in Spanish.

'Of course I know Juan Francisco. Who are you guys, anyway?'

'I am his Uncle Juan,' the short fat one said. 'And this is his Uncle Carlos, and this is his Uncle Salvador.'

'Well, I'm pleased to meet you,' Flanagan said, shaking hands. 'Who's dealing?'

'We wish to pay Juan Francisco's bill,' the short fat Cuban, Uncle Juan, said.

'And we don't seem to have brought enough money,' Uncle Salvador said. 'I had heard that medical costs had gone up, but this is ridiculous.'

'I am beginning to change my opinion about the noble Dr. Hawkeye,' Uncle Carlos said.

'What's with you, Hawkeye?' Esther Flanagan said rather coldly.

'Flanagan, please tell them that Horsey paid the bill,' Hawkeye said. Flanagan did so.

'They want to give the money back,' Flanagan reported.

'That would hurt Horsey's feelings,' Trapper John said. 'Tell them that.'

She did.

'They want to know what they should do with it, then,' Flanagan reported.

'Nurse Flanagan . . .' Trapper John began with a smile.

'Shut up, Trapper,' Flanagan said quickly, and then turned to the uncles and gave a little speech, the only parts of which Trapper John and Hawkeye understood were the

21

words 'Ms. Prudence MacDonald Memorial School of Nursing.'*

The uncles looked at each other, raised their eyebrows, nodded, picked up the money and the traveller's cheques, and then smiled at Hawkeye and Trapper John.

Uncle Carlos said something to Hawkeye, and then gave him a little bow.

'What did he say?' Hawkeye asked, bowing back.

'He apologises for thinking you were a bandit,' Flanagan said. 'And they will be happy to make a contribution in your name to the Ms. Prudence MacDonald Memorial School of Nursing, of New Orleans.'

'Did you tell him that Ms. Prudence MacDonald is still among the living?' Trapper John inquired.

'I told him that it's a fine school of nursing for girls who have little money, and that it's in Horsey's hometown,' Flanagan said. 'That was enough.'

'She's right, Trapper,' Hawkeye said. 'Now let's eat.'

Over dinner, with Flanagan translating, Hawkeye and Trapper John learned that sometimes the term refugee is a trifle misleading. While uncles Salvador, Juan, and Carlos — as well as Juan Francisco — were indeed refugees from Fidel Castro's Cuba, they were not what one could term welfare clients.

They had brought with them to Miami, in lieu of material goods, the talent and ambition that had made them successful in Cuba. After an initial period during which they had worked as a waiter (Carlos), busboy (Juan), and dishwasher

---

*The chief of nursing education at the MacDonald School of Nursing was Margaret Houlihan Wachauf Wilson, R.N., Lt. Col., Army Nurse Corps, Retired, who had once served in the 4077th MASH with Doctors Pierce and McIntyre. The details of her postwar career may be found, for those with an interest in the life of a retiree, in *M*A*S*H Goes to New Orleans* and in her pseudononymous autobiography, *God, Medicine and Me*, by 'Reverend Mother Emeritus', published by the Joyful Practices Press, Manhattan, Kansas. (It is 356 pages long, illustrated, and has an index.)

(Salvador) in one of Miami Beach's most famous hotels, they had gone into business for themselves.

To cut what was a long story short, Uncle Salvador now occupied the owner's penthouse in the Miami Beach hotel where he had once washed dishes. The hotel was a wholly-owned subsidiary of Cuba Libre Enterprises, Inc., of which Uncle Juan was president and Uncle Carlos chairman of the board. They were involved in hotels, wholesale foods, housing developments, and even an airline.

When Juan Francisco had finally been smuggled out of Cuba with his mother, it had been decided that the first thing the boy had to do was learn to speak English. It had also been decided that the worst place for him to learn English was in Miami, where the residents almost without exception had noticeable accents – Southern, or Spanish, or Bronx.

Uncle Salvador, who had become a Boy Scout executive, solved the problem neatly while attending a scout executives' conference in Washington, D.C. There, he was assured by a scout executive from Maine that the inhabitants of Maine spoke English of such purity and clarity that the Crown Prince of England came there, incognito, to brush up. Getting Juan Francisco into Camp Kitatinny had been simple to arrange.

When Dr. Pierce and Dr. McIntyre, not without effort, finally succeeded in pushing uncles Carlos, Juan, and Salvador into their chartered jet, the two doctors felt that the Juan Francisco incident was closed. It had been an even more pleasant vignette in the practice of medicine than they had first thought. Not only had the patient recovered fully, he had turned out to be, instead of a poor and lonely refugee, a refugee with a large, loving and loaded family.

And again, they thought that would be the end of it.

They erred.

Ten days later, they received official notice that there were now in the Ms. Prudence MacDonald Memorial School of Nursing something known as the Doctors Pierce and

McIntyre Memorial Scholarships. The scholarships had been established by the Cuba Libre Enterprises, Inc., Foundation in their names. A bequest had been made large enough to provide, from earnings, full-tuition scholarships for two deserving young women who wished to become registered nurses.

Now, in addition to Uncle Carlos, Uncle Juan, and Uncle Salvador, little Juan Francisco had an aunt, known to all but her brothers as Doña Antoinetta. There are three titles to describe the gentle sex in Spanish. 'Señorita' is an unmarried woman. 'Señora' is a married woman. 'Doña' is a title applied to ladies who have earned great respect and who enjoy unusual prestige. The matriarch of a family, say, pushing eighty, who reigns over a flock of sons and daughters, grandsons and granddaughters, nieces, nephews, cousins, and other assorted kin is sometimes accorded the title of Doña.

Doña Antoinetta met all these criteria save one. Without question, she reigned over the family Gomez y Sanchez. It was she who had made the decision that the family must flee Cuba to seek a new life in the United States. It was she who had arranged for the boat that had carried them to Florida. It was Doña Antoinetta who had arranged for a small package of tobacco seeds to be smuggled out of Cuba to be planted in the Honduras – the seeds that formed the basis of Cuba Libre Enterprises, Inc.

It was to Doña Antoinetta that everyone in the family Gomez y Sanchez turned for advice, for approval, and, most important, for permission to do anything at all. A tall lady, amply bosomed, given to severe black dresses and no makeup whatsoever, she lived quietly, devoting her life to her family and her church.

But Doña Antoinetta was not a grandmother. She wasn't even a mother. She had never married, and she was just this side of fifty. There had once been a man in her life; it had been a tragic episode of which she never spoke, and about

24

which no one, not even — or perhaps, especially — her brothers dared ask.

When the Cuba Libre Enterprises, Inc., Grumman Gulfstream on which uncles Carlos, Juan, and Salvador had flown to Spruce Harbour, Maine, returned to Miami International Airport and taxied to a stop, Doña Antoinetta was waiting for it, sitting in the back seat of a black Cadillac limousine, her long pale fingers touching the crucifix she wore on a fine gold chain around her neck.

The first brother to reach the door of the aircraft, Uncle Juan (properly Juan Alphonos Gregorio Gomez y Sanchez), winced when he saw the familiar limousine. But then he forced a smile on his face, walked toward the limousine, and got into same.

Doña Antoinetta leaned forward to give her brother her soft, pale white cheek to kiss.

'Juanito,' Doña Antoinetta barked, in ever so gentle a voice, 'do I detect the odour of fermented malt liquor on your person?'

'The natives of Maine have strange customs, dear sister,' Uncle Juan said.

'Indeed?'

'The doctors who treated little Juanito refused money,' Juan said.

'And what has that to do with your returning smelling of fish and beer?'

'It is a long story, dear sister.'

'We will listen to your story, Juanito, after we stop by the church and pick up Father Pedro,' she said.

'Father Pedro?'

'Not only am I sure the good father will be interested in the quaint customs of the natives of Maine, but I don't think you'd dare lie about them to him,' Doña Antoinetta said very softly. Then she looked out the window. She reached across her brother to the door and pushed a button; the window whooshed down.

'Carlos!' she called.

25

'Yes, dear sister?'

'Salvador?'

'Yes, sister dear?'

'If you two smell anything like this beer-soaked blot on the escutcheon of the family Gomez y Sanchez, be good enough to find a taxi.'

'Yes, of course, dear sister,' Uncle Salvador and Uncle Carlos said, in duet.

Doña Antoinetta caused the window to ascend. She spoke to the chauffeur: 'Please telephone to Father Pedro,' she said, 'and inform him that I would be profoundly grateful if he could spare the family Gomez y Sanchez an hour of his time. Ask him to be prepared to take confession from three sinners.'

'Sí, Doña Antoinetta,' the chauffeur said, reaching for the radio telephone.

CHAPTER THREE

Father Pedro Huaretto sat in what looked like an attitude of prayer at the Gomez y Sanchez family table in the penthouse atop the Winter Palace Hotel.* Father Pedro was a roly-poly cleric, quite bald, wearing glasses and a black tropical worsted suit. His fingertips were touching, and his head was bent over them.

He raised his eyes slightly. Directly across the wide oak table were the brothers, looking much as they had looked, long years before, in school in Cuba. That is to say, they were waiting for the boom to fall on them.

At the head of the table, one hand resting on a crystal water glass, the other touching the crucifix at her neck, sat Doña Antoinetta. Finally, Father Pedro spoke.

'Under the circumstances, Doña Antoinetta,' he said, 'I don't see what else Salvador, Carlos, and Juan could have done. Refusing an offer of hospitality, particularly from men to whom one acknowledges a debt, would have been very discourteous.'

'You are willing to believe, Father,' Doña Antoinetta said, 'their story that two *doctors*, two men pledged to ease

*The former owner of the Winter Palace (sixty stories of plate glass, plaster statuary, and phony marble on the Miami beach) had realized that the owners of the Fountainbleau, down the street a little, had had a good idea in naming their operation after the palace of the kings of France. A little research had turned up the information that the Russians had had their own elegant establishment, called the Winter Palace because the czar had wintered there. The new owners, Cuba Libre Enterprises, Inc., had kept the name on, assuming possession for several reasons, including the very good one that changing the name would mean buying a new sign. The existing sign was twenty stories tall and in seven colours of neon reminded vacationing Yankees how lucky they were to be in sunny Miami, enjoying a Russian Winter Palace minus the blizzards.

27

suffering, actually pressed beer upon them, beer in such vast quantities?'

'I do,' he said. 'Their customs are strange to us – as they proved by refusing the offer to pay for services to little Juan Francisco.'

'Which brings us to that,' Doña Antoinetta said. 'How may we discharge that debt of honour, Father?'

'That should pose no problem,' Father Pedro said. 'The suggestion offered was that a contribution be made to this home for nurses. That would seem to be a fair discharge of obligation.'

'Far be it from me to question your wisdom, Father,' Doña Antoinetta began – and Father Pedro looked at her, wondering what she could possibly find wrong with giving money to a home for student nurses. 'But what do we know about this Ms. Prudence MacDonald Memorial School of Nursing?'

'Nothing but what we have been told,' Father Pedro admitted.

'We now know they have strange customs in Maine,' Doña Antoinetta said. 'Would it not be your advice, then, that we inquire into the nature and reputation of the school?'

'That wouldn't hurt,' Father Pedro admitted.

'Oh, Father Pedro!' Doña Antoinetta said, pushing a telephone across the table to him. 'I don't know what the family Gomez y Sanchez would do without your sage and wise counsel.'

'I really wouldn't know where to begin,' Father Pedro said.

'Try the archdiocese,' Doña Antoinetta said, smiling one of her warm and utterly terrifying smiles. 'Perhaps the chancellor would be good enough to tell you what he knows.'

Three minutes later, the telephone on the desk of Monsignor John Joseph Clancy, Chancellor of the Archdiocese of New Orleans, rang.

Monsignor Clancy took the call reluctantly. He had only recently returned from a trying business luncheon. Twice a month he met with Father Jacques dePresseps, pastor of the Church of the Immaculate Conception, Bayou Perdu, La. (and, more importantly, chaplain to the Bayou Perdu Council, Knights of Columbus). The luncheon had been at Brennan's Restaurant, a little gift from one of Father dePresseps' more affluent parishioners, one Col. Jean-Pierre de la Chevaux. Col. de la Chevaux also served as Grand Exalted Royal Keeper of the Golden Fleece for the Bayou Perdu Council, K. of C., which was sort of a mixed blessing. . . .

For nearly two hundred years, the Church of the Immaculate Conception, Bayou Perdu, had been something of a problem, money-wise, to the diocese. A small building of rough-hewn timber perched precariously on pilings above Bayou Perdu, it served the three-hundred-odd Cajuns who had lived in the area since the time of Evangeline, barely existing on what fish and crawfish they could extract from the swamp and what deer, possum, and other wildlife they could reap with a grand disregard for hunting regulations. What little cash there had been had come from the illegal distillation of corn liquor.

The diocese had been forced to financially underwrite the cost of maintaining the parish and the small parochial school, and had made quiet donations to the Bayou Perdu Council, Knights of Columbus, in the belief that membership in the Knights served to uplift the morals of the male members of the community.

All that had been changed by progress, specifically the interstate highway program. The federal government had wished to build a super-highway from the Texas border to the Mississippi border. A search of real-estate documents dating back to the French land grants had revealed that some fifty thousand acres of land (actually swamp, described by the U.S. Army Corps of Engineers as 'swamp, and quicksand, unfit for cultivation or any other purpose, save perhaps an alligator refuge') had come down through the years, free of any encumbrance, to one Jean-Pierre de la Chevaux. . . .

Aside from a two-year tour of duty in the army, where he had acquired the wounds necessary to qualify him for a pension, several medals, and a taste for a particularly powerful potion known as Old White Stagg Blended Kentucky Bourbon, Jean-Pierre ('Horsey') de la Chevaux had never left Bayou Perdu or held a job, and had shown no inclination to do either. He was prepared to go through life as his ancestors had — poaching deer, making White Lightning, and more or less settling down with some comely Cajun to propagate the race.

But the Feds were not to be denied. They demanded, before advancing their ninety-nine-percent share of the cost of the super-highway, that Louisiana hold clear title to the land on which the highway was to be built. That meant securing a right-of-way through the fifty thousand acres of swamp owned by ex-Sgt. de la Chevaux.

Securing this right-of-way proved rather difficult. For one thing, the first governmental functionaries sent, by airboat, to discuss the matter with Mr. de la Chevaux were mistaken for functionaries of the Alcohol Tax Unit, known as Revenuers. The airboats were attacked by weapons including six Browning automatic rifles and two .50-calibre machine guns that Sgt. de la Chevaux had had the foresight to ship home in small pieces from Korea.

It was at this point that Father dePresseps entered the picture. The priest then in charge of the Church of the Immaculate Conception was an Irishman. There was what psychologists called a 'personality clash' between the good father and his charges. After he suggested that Horsey and others at least talk to the men from the government, and even consider abandoning the illegal distillation of spirits, he was set adrift in a hollowed-out log (a pirogue) with enough smoked venison and other provisions to last him until he eventually floated down to New Orleans.

He was, in fact, plucked from the mighty Mississippi at the foot of Canal Street, and immediately begged the archbishop for an assignment to a cloistered monastery.

Two days later, after some remarkably fast paperwork through the Vatican, Father dePresseps arrived from Normandy. The Cajuns had originally been Normans, and when Father dePresseps spoke to them in a familiar accent, they were willing to take his word for it that he wasn't an undercover agent for the Revenuers.

At Father dePresseps' suggestion, negotiations were undertaken with the state concerning a right-of-way through de la Chevaux land. A price of fifty thousand dollars was finally agreed upon. The New Orleans *Picaroon-Statesman* referred to the purchase as 'an unconscionable rape of the state treasury,' but it was either pay Horsey or not build the highway, and the cheque was delivered.

The diocese was at first delighted. Under Father dePresseps' guidance, Mr. de la Chevaux decided that with the exception of the price of a new chain saw, a new outboard motor for his pirogue, and the drilling of a new water well by Sears, Roebuck & Company, he would turn over the balance of the fifty thousand dollars to Father dePresseps, who would apportion the money between the church, which needed both new pilings and a new roof, and the parish school, which had similar pressing needs.

Then the crew from Sears appeared to drill the well. They encountered something they hadn't expected, and it incidentally resulted in the total loss of their drilling equipment. What their simple little drilling bit encountered, eight feet beneath the surface of Bayou Perdu, was 'the largest pool of natural gas ever discovered in the western hemisphere.'

The first cheque, an advance against future royalties, came to just over a million dollars. A check for ten percent of that amount, a tithe, was delivered to the Chancellory of the Archdiocese of New Orleans the next day. Horsey had been taught to tithe by his late beloved *grandmère*, and he had done so all his life. The tenth poached deer, the tenth gallon of White Lightning, the tenth pail of crawfish had always been set aside for the Church, and a tenth of income would be set aside now. The only difference now was that a certified

31

cheque didn't have to be hung and drawn and skinned, or run through a barrel of charcoal, or pursued on one's knees in a ditch.

The archbishop, while of course grateful for a cheque for one hundred thousand dollars, nevertheless had second thoughts. As he confided to Monsignor John Joseph Clancy:

'You know, Jack, I really hate to take this. I don't mean to sound cynical, but I'll bet you my two tickets to the next Saints game that Horsey de la Chevaux will be parted from all that money before the year's out.'

Monsignor Clancy was forced to agree. Certainly a simple Cajun whose only excursion away from his bayou had been into the army would not be able to hold his own in the cold, ruthless, and sometimes outright dishonest world of high finance.

His Eminence and the Right Reverend Father were wrong. Horsey de la Chevaux, while frankly a bit crude, was not at all stupid. He was, moreover, the scion of a family that had for more than two hundred years been at war with the established forces of law and order. And he now had the sage advice of Father dePresseps to draw upon. No *summa cum laude* graduate of the Harvard School of Business, no matter how dedicated to the principle that thievery is the name of the game, was anywhere close to a match for a Louisiana Cajun getting advice from a Norman peasant priest.

Within two years of the discovery of the pool of natural gas, Chevaux Petroleum Corporation, International, had joined the list of the five hundred companies in the world. Within five years, it had joined the exclusive One Hundred Club.

There were some benefits to the diocese in addition to the tithe. The Church of the Immaculate Conception was rebuilt. The unpainted pine structure supported on pilings was replaced with a marble edifice bearing a strong resemblance to St. Peter's Church in Venice. The parish school was transformed from a primitive one-room place into a multi-million-dollar edifice, which, with the aid of a professor formerly associated with the Missouri School of Mines, taught petro-geology.

The Bayou perdu Council K. of C. Council House, which had, if anything, been even more rickety than the Church of the Immaculate Conception, was now a stone and marble structure housing, among other things, six bowling alleys, an indoor skeet range, and the longest bar in the United States. (The bar had been purchased from a to-be-torn-down hotel in Milwaukee, disassembled, and flown to Louisiana over the violent protests of the Save Our Wisconsin Historical Heritage Association, which felt it belonged in a museum.)

Some of the blessings were mixed. Before 'The Discovery,' as it came to be known, the Bayou Perdu Council, K. of C., had existed more or less on the charity of its more prosperous brother councils within the consistory. Its members had, B.D., been uniformed in perfectly satisfactory, if somewhat faded, uniforms acquired from a used-clothing dealer. (They had seen previous service as usher suits for the New York World's Fair of 1939–40.)

In response to a summons from the Grand Exalted Royal Keeper of the Golden Fleece, accompanied by a cheque for twenty-five thou as earnest money, a somewhat effeminate travelling salesman flew by chartered private jet to the newly constructed Bayou Perdu International Airport to fit the Knights in uniforms more in keeping with their new affluence.

The new uniforms, resplendent with gold braid, gold lace, and glistening swords, and featuring hats patterned after those worn by Admiral Nelson at the Battle of Trafalgar, were without question the most splendiferous ever worn by the Knights of Columbus – or for that matter, anyone, anywhere.

As the uniform salesman's jet took off, another jet landed, this one bearing a salesman from the firm that sold buses to the Greyhound people. Horsey de la Chevaux had learned that while one might put a Knight behind the wheel of a new Eldorado, one couldn't make him stay on the roads, especially after any sort of K. of C. function at which intoxicating beverages had been disbursed.

Six buses arrived a month after the salesman's visit. Patterned generally after those used by Greyhound, these vehicles were equipped with seats purchased from the people who made the first-class seats for Boeing 747 aircraft. (Mr. de la Chevaux's company now owned three Boeing 747s, as well as thirty-six other aircraft.)

The buses had, in addition to on-board restroom facilities and en-route television, fully equipped bars and storage space for the musical instruments of the Bayou Perdu Council, K. of C., Marching Band. They were painted a brilliant yellow, and on their roofs were batteries of silver-plated airhorns that, when special buttons were pushed, played 'Onward, Christian Soldiers!'

There was some grumbling in the ranks of other councils of the Knights that eventually reached His Eminence. Mr. de la Chevaux was escorted into the archbishop's presence by Father dePresseps.

The litany of complaints from other councils was brought up. Certainly, the archbishop said, there was some merit the complaints of the other Knights that the all-around aura of dignity, nobility, and Christian service of the Knights of Columbus was tarnished by the Bayou Perdu Council's behaviour.

'Not that I mind, of course, Horsey,' His Eminence said. 'I rather like "There'll Be a Hot Time in the Old Town Tonight," even when played on three trumpets, four bass drums, two tubas, six kazoos, and a glockenspiel, but do you really think it's appropriate for the annual Feast of the Assumption Processional? The choice of music; the suspiciously, staggeringly cheerful condition of the musicians; and, to be blunt, the baton twirlers in what must be described as *extremely* abbreviated costumes *has* caused some talk.'

'Horsey's sorry, Archbishop,' Mr. de la Chevaux replied. 'It'll never happen again.'

'That's very good of you.'

34

'The Bayou Perdu Council, K. of C., is out of business as of right now,' Horsey went on.

'I don't really think it's necessary to go that far, Horsey,' the archbishop replied.

'It's now the Bayou Perdu Council, Knights of Bienville,' Horsey said. 'We been talking about it, anyway.'

'I don't quite understand you, Horsey,' the archbishop said.

'Well, a couple of things, Archbishop. We're not so dumb. We know the other Knights think we're a bunch of bums. But the real thing is, we don't think we belong in the Knights of Columbus.'

'But of course you do,' the archbishop said.

'Nah,' Horsey replied. 'Columbus was an Eyetalian who landed on Cuba and thought it was India.'

'Yes, that's true,' the archbishop said.

'Bienville, though,' Horsey went on. 'He was a Frenchman, like us. And he discovered Mobile and New Orleans. He didn't think he was in India. He knew better. I got some of the shysters drawing up the papers.'

'I think that the gentlemen who practice law would prefer to be called "attorneys", Horsey,' the archbishop said.

'What I pay them, I'll call them what I want. You can stop worrying, Archbishop, the Bayou Perdu Council, K. of C., ain't ever gonna embarrass the archbishop no more.'

It took all of the archbishop's considerable powers of persuasion to convince Horsey that he and the Knights belonged in the K. of C., and then to convince the rest of the Louisiana Consistory — finally, to announce *ex cathedra* — that the Bayou Perdu Council belonged, and would remain, in the consistory. . . .

Two months after that, shortly after being appointed colonel on the governor's staff, Horsey took the archbishop fishing. Not, as the archbishop had expected, on the new seventy-four-foot diesel yacht *Evangeline* Chevaux Petroleum had acquired to ferry its crewmen to and from its offshore drilling platforms, but in his pirogue.

As the two sat in a remote corner of the bayou quietly hoping to attract the attention of a channel catfish, Horsey spoke. The archbishop, who had known Horsey since Horsey had been a student at St. Paul's School for Unmanageable Boys, had known that something was on his mind.

'Archbishop,' Horsey said. 'I been thinking.'

'About what, Horsey?'

'All the trouble me and the guys caused you, the embarrassment and all.'

'Oh, don't worry about it, Horsey. I'm sure that you're going to try harder in the future.'

'We sent the baton twirlers back to the Hotsy-Totsy Club on Bourbon Street,' Horsey said. 'But I want to do a little something to make it up to you.'

'What did you have in mind, Horsey?' the archbishop asked, somewhat warily.

'How about a hospital?' Horsey said.

'A hospital?'

'It would have to be a secret between you and me,' Horsey said. 'I wouldn't want anyone to know.'

'A *hospital*?' the archbishop repeated. 'Do you know what hospitals *cost*, Horsey?'

'I had one of my shysters find out for me.' Horsey reached into his shirt pocket, pulled open the drawstring on his bag of Bull Durham, and extracted a crumpled piece of paper. 'Here's enough to get it started,' he said, handing His Eminence a certified cheque. 'Let me know when you need some more.'

The cheque was for three and a half million dollars. . . .

The Gates of Heaven Hospital opened its doors a year later. Horsey never changed his mind about keeping it a secret. He would be happy knowing he'd provided the money, he said, and given it a name. Neither the archbishop nor Reverend Mother Superior Bernadette of Lourdes, M.D., F.A.C.S., its chief of staff, could bring themselves to suggest that the name Horsey had chosen might possibly be misinterpreted.

CHAPTER FOUR

Over lunch at Brennan's, Monsignor John Joseph Clancy had learned, to his considerable and undisguised relief, that the previous two weeks had been relatively uneventful for parishioners of the Church of the Immaculate Conception and the Bayou Perdu Council, Knights of Columbus. There had been two births, one death, and a marriage. Since the christening celebrations and wedding reception had been held in the Bayou Perdu Council House, no merry revellers had had a confrontation with the forces of the law. The sheriff of Bayou Perdu Parish, moreover, who looked fondly upon the Bayou Perdu Council, K. of C., especially since they had presented him with a black-and-white Cadillac Fleetwood limousine for a patrol car, had been very understanding about what had taken place at the wake. He had simply 'detained' a dozen people overnight in the bastille, and had filed no official charges for public drunkenness, inciting to riot, or using provoking language to a sheriff in the execution of his official office.

'I only got one bum in the slammer,' Father dePresseps reported. It was a source of some annoyance to the monsignor that what little English Father dePresseps had picked up was mostly vernacular.

'Who's that?'

'François Mulligan,' Father dePresseps said.

'And what did François do to incur the displeasure of the authorities?' Monsignor Clancy asked. He was a bit ashamed to realise that he was really curious — personally curious, rather than professionally interested in the woes of one of his flock.

François Mulligan was one of the few inhabitants of Bayou Perdu who had spent much time, B.D., away from the bayou. Mocked as a child because of his mixed

37

blood,* François had run off at sixteen to join the Marines.

At the Parris Island recruit depot, Mulligan had become something of an instant celebrity. A long-cherished Marine tradition is for a close-combat drill instructor to toss a bayonet to a recruit with the admonition, 'Try to kill me.' Normally, the recruit somewhat timidly attacks the D.I., and instantly finds himself flat on his back, whereupon the drill instructor can proceed with the instruction,

'Izzat an ordair, sair?' sixteen-year-old François had politely inquired in his thick bayou dialect.

'That's an order!' the drill instructor had barked, delighted that he had a cocky recruit to tame.

Fortunately the drill instructor, to maintain the erect posture and flat stomach expected of drill instructors, was wearing, under his stiffly starched uniform, an undergarment constructed of thick rubber and canvas reinforced with steel strips. For, with a quick flip of his wrist, François had sent the gleaming bayonet spinning end over end toward the drill instructor, so that when it came to rest, the point, protruding through layers of canvas, rubber, and steel strips, drew just a little bit of blood from the D.I.'s navel.

'My God!' the drill instructor had cried.

'It is nothin', sair,' François had said modestly. 'Actually, I am one of zee worst knife-throwers of Bayou Perdu.'

Twenty years later, after a distinguished career, Master Chief Gunnery Sergeant François Mulligan, U.S.-M.C., retired from the Corps and returned to Bayou Perdu. He was welcomed, of course, into the Bayou Perdu Council, K. of C., where his natural talents (he was six-five and weighed three hundred pounds) were recognized in his appointment as Grand Exalted Knight Guardian of the Sacred Serenity, a

---

*His father was 'Bitter Ed' Mulligan, an Irish bootlegger from New Jersey who had come to Bayou Perdu for a load of White Lightning never dreaming that a little dalliance with a comely Cajun would see him propped up with a double-barrelled L. C. Smith 12-bore before the altar of the Church of the Immaculate Conception as the wedding vows were recited.

position that in another body would have been entitled 'sergeant-at-arms.'

There was not a Knight in the Bayou Perdu Council who could muster the courage to deny Grand Exalted Knight Guardian of the Sacred Serenity Mulligan's soft-voiced entreaties (which were generally phrased, 'Shut up, youse bums!'), for François expected the same instant, unquestioning obedience from his fellow Knights that he had grown accustomed to as a Master Chief Gunnery Sergeant, U.S.M.C., and he became rather spectacularly violent when he didn't get it.

He became, after The Discovery, one of the first employees of Chevaux Petroleum Corporation, International. Horsey took him from the bar of the Council House the day the pool was discovered and asked him to keep the curious away from the well-head.

He was now carried on the rolls of the corporation as Vice-President, Employee Relations. He travelled the globe (Chevaux Petroleum operated in sixteen different countries) settling the little disputes that from time to time arose between Chevaux employees and their supervisors. . . .

'You sure talk funny, Monsignor, you know dat?' Father dePresseps said.

'What I meant to ask, Father,' Monsignor Clancy clarified, 'is, why is François in the slammer?'

'The usual reason,' Father dePresseps replied. 'He said something he shouldn't have about some broad.'

'Could you be more specific?'

'François, he don't like Latin broads,' Father dePresseps explained.

'Father, please don't take offence, but I would like to suggest that the term "broad" is somewhat derogatory. . . .'

'You know it!' Father dePresseps said, 'Ol' François can't stand them Latin broads.'

'Go on,' The monsignor said.

'Well, he was down at site fifty-six, in Venezuela, and there was some sort of party . . . you sure you really want to hear all this, Monsignor?'

39

'I think I should,' the monsignor replied.

'Well, one of the guests heard what François was saying about Latin broads at the bar. . . .'

'And what was that?'

'I'm a priest. I don't like to use words like dat,' Father dePresseps said.

'I understand,' the monsignor said. 'So what happened?'

'They had to call out the Venezuelan National Guard,' Father dePresseps said. 'To stop it. Six of our guys, and twenty-one of theirs, went to the hospital. The bill for damages to the hotel came to about six thousand bucks, and, for a while, they were going to shoot François. But Horsey talked the president into a presidential pardon, on the condition that we don't never send François back to Venezuela. He should get outta the slammer tomorrow.'

'And where is François going then?'

'Horsey's gonna send him to the North Slope in Alaska,' Father dePresseps replied. 'François gets along O.K. with the Eskimo broads.'

François, in fact, the monsignor remembered, got along with most ladies rather well. Far too well, actually. In point of fact, the only man who got along better than François with ladies of various shapes, nationalities, and descriptions was the archbishop's favourite opera singer, Boris Alexandrovich Korsky-Rimsakov, whose activities in that area were something of a legend.

It was only with Spanish-speaking females that François had difficulty. The sound of a soft Spanish voice or a glimpse of dark Spanish eyes was enough to turn what was normally a rather shy man (in the presence of females) into a woman-hater.

'But it would be your judgment, Father,' the monsignor went on, 'that, presuming François is released from confinement tomorrow, that the incident is over?'

'Yeah, all we gotta do is make sure that we keep François away from Latin broads,' Father dePresseps said. He had then turned over to the monsignor the three week^l-

cheques. The first cheque was the tithe payment from Chevaux Petroleum Corporation, International. The second cheque represented twenty percent of the profits from the operation of the canteens operated by the Bayou Perdu Council, K. of C., in Bayou Perdu and in twenty-eight locations around the world. The third was the Conscience Fund cheque. The Bayou Perdu Council, K. of C., each week presented to the Archdiocese of New Orleans a cheque matching the fines paid by its members to various courts all over the world.

This third cheque was for $1,150. Monsignor Clancy glanced at it, thought that it was a bit small, and was a little disappointed. Just in time, he remembered what the cheque represented, and stopped himself from commenting on its unusually low dollar value.

The two clerics finished the brandy with which they were concluding their lunch, and then went back to their places of work — Father dePresseps by helicopter from the roof of the Cheavaux Petroleum International Building on Canal Street, Monsignor Clancy by motorcycle to the office of the chancellory. . . .

He had been back in the office only a few minutes when Sister Fortitude, his faithful and efficient secretary, told him there was a Spanish-sounding priest from Miami on the phone asking about the Ms. Prudence MacDonald Memorial School of Nursing.

'Monsignor J. J. Clancy at your service, Father,' Clancy said when he finally picked up the phone. 'How may I help you?'

'Father Pedro Huaretto, Monsignor. I speak for the family Gomez y Sanchez.'

'And how may I assist the family Gomez y Sanchez?' Monsignor Clancy replied.

'It's the other way around, Monsignor. The family Gomez y Sanchez wishes to make a contribution to a New Orleans medical institution.'

'Indeed?'

41

'Are you familiar with the Ms. Prudence MacDonald Memorial School of Nursing, Monsignor?'

'Why, yes, I am,' Monsignor Clancy replied.

'And is it a reputable institution?'

'Quite reputable,' Monsignor Clancy said. 'In point of fact, it is the nursing school connected with our own Gates of Heaven Hospital.'

'Well, I'm glad to hear that, from you, sir,' Father Huaretto said.

'May I ask how the school came to the attention of the family Gomez y Sanchez, Father?'

'It is a debt of honour, Monsignor,' Father Huaretto said.

'Oh?'

'A splendid Christian gentleman from New Orleans paid a hospital bill for a member of the family, in the belief that he could not pay it himself.'

'Well, isn't that nice? I don't mean to boast, Father, but we try here, from the pulpit, to remind our good people of the Good Samaritan. You didn't mention the Samaritan's name?'

'De la Chevaux, Monsignor. Horsey de la Chevaux.'

'Oh, yes,' the monsignor said. 'I'm acquainted with Mr. de la Chevaux.'

'The family is naturally curious, Monsignor, about Ms. MacDonald,' Father Huaretto said. 'How long has it been since she's gone to paradise?'

'I'll tell you what I'm going to do, Father Huaretto,' Monsignor Clancy said, suddenly turning white in the face. 'I'm going to connect you with the archbishop himself. Will you hold a minute, please?'

He covered the microphone with his hand and pushed the intercom switch.

'Your Eminence, are you free?'

'What's on your mind, Jack?'

'I got a priest on the line speaking for a family who wants to make a donation to the Ms. Prudence MacDonald Memorial School of Nursing.'

'Splendid!' the archbishop said

'He wants to know when Prudence went to paradise,' the monsignor said.

'Oh,' the archbishop replied.

'I told him you'd tell him,' the monsignor said.

'Thanks a lot, Jack,' the archbishop said. 'If I didn't know better, I'd think you'd been off on another of your regular twice-a-month liquid lunches with Father dePresseps.'

'As a matter of fact, Your Eminence . . .'

'Put him on,' the archbishop said. 'I'll handle it.'

'Thank you, Your Eminence.'

The archbishop picked up his phone.

'This is the archbishop,' he said. 'I understand that you're interested in the Ms. Prudence MacDonald Memorial School of Nursing.'

'Actually, Your Eminence, since Monsignor Clancy has assured me that it is a reputable institution, I'm more curious about the Blessed Prudence MacDonald herself.'

'And a splendid institution it is,' the archbishop went on. 'It serves as the nurse-training facility for our Gates of Heaven Hospital.'

'And what about the Blessed Prudence?' Father Huaretto pursued.

'Actually, Father, that's a question of semantics. While there is no doubt in my mind that Prudence is blessed, lower case b, she is not – at least not yet – Blessed, capital B.'

'Forgive me, Your Eminence,' Father Huaretto said. 'I don't quite follow you.'

'I'll tell you what I'm going to do, Father,' the archbishop said. 'I'm going to transfer you to the office of the chief of staff of Gates of Heaven Hospital, Reverend Mother Superior Bernadette of Lourdes, M.D., F.A.C.S. I'm sure that she'll be able to answer your questions satisfactorily. Would you hold on a moment, please?'

He pushed the HOLD button on his telephone, picked up another telephone, dialled hastily, and waited impatiently. 'This is the archbishop,' he said. 'Connnect me immediately with Reverend Mother Superior Bernadette of Lourdes.'

There was a pause.

'Hello?' a female voice said impatiently.

'This is the archbishop. I wish to speak to Reverend Mother Superior Bernadette of Lourdes.'

'I knew it would either be a major medical catastrophe or you,' the female voice said.

'I didn't recognize your voice, Bernie,' the archbishop said. 'I hope I'm not interrupting anything?'

'I just jerked a gallbladder, Paul,' the Reverend Mother said. 'One of the surgical residents can close. What's on your mind?'

'You're in the operating room?'

'You got it, Paul,' she said. 'What's the big flap?'

'We've got a little problem, Bernie,' the archbishop said. 'One right down your alley.'

'Shoot.'

'I've got a priest on the line, speaking for a family who wishes to make a contribution to the Ms. Prudence MacDonald Memorial School of Nursing.'

'That's a problem? They can sure use the dough. I was going over the books with Margaret just the other day. You have no idea how much food sixty healthy young females can put away, Paul.'

'And how is Margaret?' the archbishop asked.

'What's the problem, Paul?' the Reverend Mother asked.

'They want to know when Prudence went to paradise,' the archbishop said.

She laughed.

'What's so funny?' the archbishop demanded sharply. 'What am I supposed to tell him?'

'Prudence was there — getting some female-type advice from Margaret about the care and feeding of husbands — when I saw Margaret. I asked her how she liked being married, and she said it was paradise.'

'I don't think that's exactly the paradise Father Huaretto of Miami and the family Gomez y Sanchez have in mind, Bernie.'

(It should, in the interests of clarity, be parenthetically noted here that the Ms. Prudence MacDonald Memorial School of Nursing, formerly the New Orleans Christian Mental and Physical Centre, and, prior to that, Madame Eloise's Sporting House, a well-known New Orleans landmark, was established as one of the major – in fact, the only – good works of the American Tonsil, Adenoid and Vas Deferens Society. Ms. MacDonald, then a journalist in the employ of the New Orleans *Picaroon-Statesman*, had come into the possession of certain information concerning the TA & VD Society. In exchange for her promise not to publish this information, the TA & VD Society had purchased the building from its former owners and placed it at the disposal of the Reverend Mother Emeritus Margaret Houlihan Wachauf Wilson, R.N., of the God Is Love in All Forms Christian Church, Inc., for use as a nursing school. A name for the new institution being required, it was decided between the Reverend Mother Emeritus and Doctors Hawkeye Pierce and Trapper John McIntyre, who were involved in the negotiations, that it was fitting to name the school after Ms. Prudence MacDonald. Not only had she been responsible for the TA & VD Society's remarkable generosity, but she was about to enter into the bonds of matrimony, to exchange her name for that of one Lemuel 'Ace' Travers, a fellow journalist. The Reverend Mother Emeritus had felt that so naming the institution would perpetuate the name of one of New Orleans' most prominent women's libbers. Doctors Pierce and McIntyre agreed, but went a step further, at least privately. They felt that anyone who looked up at the name chiselled into the marble over the entrance to the structure would be reminded of happier times, when the place had been a sporting house.*)

*The sordid details of all this, for those with a prurient interest in such matters, have been recorded in what has been described as 'certainly an unusual style' in a neat, stoutly bound volume entitled *M*A*S*H Goes to New Orleans*. The publishers, Sphere Books, as a public service, have made this tome available on racks in better bus terminals and other gathering places of the literary cognoscenti.

'Well, what am *I* supposed to tell them?' Reverend Mother Superior Bernadette of Lourdes demanded. 'If you think I'm going to do your fibbing for you, Paul, think again.'

'You're speaking to your archbishop, you know!' he said, somewhat tartly.

'Any time you're dissatisfied with my services, Paul,' the Reverend Mother said, 'I've got a standing offer from Dago Red to take over the American Hospital in Rome.'

'No offence, Bernie,' the archbishop said. 'You know we couldn't do without you. Who else could I turn to with a problem like this?'

The Reverend Mother paused thoughtfully. 'Well, they need the dough. Put him on, Paul.'

'I knew I could rely on you, Bernie,' the archbishop said. . . .

Five minutes later, Father Pedro Huaretto put the telephone down and turned to face Doña Antoinetta Gomez y Sanchez.

'Well?' she said.

'Doña Antoinetta, you may put your understandable fears to rest.'

'Indeed?'

'I have spoken not only with Monsignor Clancy, the chancellor of the archdiocese, but with His Eminence the archbishop himself.'

'Indeed?'

'*And* with the chief of staff of the Gates of Heaven Hospital, Reverend Mother Superior Bernadette of Lourdes, M.D., F.A.C.S.'

'And?'

'The Ms. Prudence MacDonald Memorial School of Nursing is a highly respected institution of impeccable reputation. Moreover, as the Reverend Mother Bernadette of Lourdes put it, 'they need the dough.'' '

'Reverend *Mother*,' said Doña Antoinetta, herself something of a closet women's libber, 'is in charge of the institution?'

'No, Doña Antoinetta, the nun in charge is the Reverend Mother Emeritus Margaret.'

'Did you speak with *her*?'

'She was not available. She is in Las Vegas, Nevada. Probably at some medical or religious conference.'

'Well, that's that, then,' Uncle Salvador said. 'Find out what a hospital around here to dress a bad cut, set a broken bone, and send this place a cheque for twice that amount.'

Doña Antoinetta began to weep. Her brothers looked very unhappy. Finally Uncle Carlos gathered his courage.

'Is something wrong, sister dear?'

'God is cruel!' Doña Antoinetta announced.

'I beg your pardon?'

'I devote myself to a life of Christian piety, with one exception which is none of anybody's business but mine, and what is my reward?'

There was no reply.

'I'll tell you what my reward is!' Doña Antoinetta said. 'Three brothers like you, that's my reward! That's my crown of thorns. Three brothers, who when faced with a matter of honour affecting the good name of the family Gomez y Sanchez and with the prospect of sixty-two devoted young women on the brink of privation and malnutrition, think more about their pocketbooks than good works. That's what my reward is!'

She dabbed at her eyes with a lace handkerchief, and continued to sob.

'Well, then, what?' Uncle Carlos asked.

'Four times what it's worth?' Uncle Juan asked.

Doña Antoinetta howled – in a ladylike manner, of course.

'Might I suggest a scholarship?' Father Huaretto suggested. Doña Antoinetta's mournful weeping stopped entirely for a moment, and then resumed at half its previous volume.

'*Two* scholarships!' Uncle Carlos cried triumphantly. 'We'll set up a trust fund!'

Doña Antoinetta stopped howling. She dried her tears with her lace handkerchief.

'Send them a small cheque,' she said. 'Say ... twenty thousand, and ask them to be good enough to come up with an adequate figure for a trust-fund endowment.'

They nodded agreement.

'And now, Father,' she said. 'Will you hear my confession?'

'Of course, Doña Antoinetta,' Father Huaretto said. Truth to tell, he wasn't looking forward to it. For twenty years now, in Cuba and in Miami, on Friday afternoons he had heard Doña Antoinetta's confessions.

It was always more or less the same confession. When Doña Antoinetta (then Señorita) had fallen from the path of righteousness and, more to the point, chastity, a quarter of a century before, she had fallen spectacularly.

Father Huaretto, himself then a young man, had been impressed with her confession at the time. Señorita Antoinetta had recalled every detail, sordid and otherwise, and every nuance, every subtle shading, in her first confession. When he had granted her absolution, he had felt that she truly recognized her errors, and that that would be the end of it.

It wasn't. While she had never repeated the offence itself, she had been unable to put it from her mind. In every confession afterwards, she had sobbingly admitted that she had been dwelling on the details of the first sin and even hoping for the opportunity to repeat the offence. Since the desire was tantamount to the act, she had been weekly in need of confession and absolution.

At first, Father Huaretto had thought that sooner or later some nice young man would come along and ask for Señorita Gomez y Sanchez' hand in marriage, and that the one indiscretion of her maidenhood would be forgotten as she assumed her natural role as wife and mother.

But, although a long line of eligible young men had sought her hand, she had never married. It was clear that she preferred the sinful memory of her first dalliance to what Father Huaretto thought of as 'the joys of matrimony.'

CHAPTER FIVE

Jimmy de Wilde, rings on his fingers and bells on the toes of his Gucci loafers, hovered nervously, reeking of My Sin, near the entrance of International Headquarters, God Is Love in All Forms Christian Church, Inc., on St. Anne Street in New Orleans. He was awaiting the return of the Rev. Mother Emeritus Margaret H. W. Wilson, presiding cleric of that religious denomination.

Mr. de Wilde served as executive secretary of the religious body and as personal secretary to the Reverend Mother Emeritus. He was, in addition, one of the founding disciples, having been present in Finnochio's Restaurant in San Francisco, California, during what *The Official History of the God Is Love in All Forms Christian Church, Inc.* referred to as The First Supper.

At The First Supper, Baxter ('Buck') Wilson (now referred to as 'Blessed Brother Buck') had announced that, after prayerful thought, he had come to see it as his duty on this earth 'to found a church for those children of God whom the extant religious bodies seem to either reject or ignore.'

The Official History said: 'The first dozen members, known as the founding disciples, included an artist, two hairdressers, a writer, two ballet dancers, a male model, an interior decorator, and the quarterback and two defensive tackles of the San Francisco Gladiators professional football team.'

Mr. de Wilde, who had just changed his name (from Oscar Dunlop, Jr.) after coming into his patrimony, had been a major financial supporter of the new religious body, and had, in fact, financed the move of its headquarters to New Orleans, Louisiana, several months later. Blessed Brother Buck had announced that New Orleans was, so to speak, virgin territory, and should be fertile ground in which the GILIAFCC, Inc., could take root.

Despite a number of problems (the New Orleans Council of Churches, to phrase it gently, reacted most uncharitably toward the GILIAFCC), the a-borning church prospered in New Orleans. The bitter editorial crusade waged against the church by the New Orleans *Picaroon-Statesman* (and Col. Beauregard C. Beaucoupmots, chairman of the board and publisher) served not to drive the GILIAFCC from the Crescent City, but rather to drive hordes of potential parishioners from their closets and through the doors of the temporary temple on Bourbon Street.

There were other problems, of course. Some of the founding disciples (who came to be known as 'the conservatives') objected bitterly to the admission of females to the church. Blessed Brother Buck, however, with the support of the 'moderate' and 'liberal' elements, insisted that the church be open to anyone who embraced its principles, without regard to race, ethnic origins, or gender proclivity.

The greatest challenge to the GILIAFCC, Inc., which for some time threatened to tear it asunder, was Blessed Brother Buck's whirlwind courtship of, and subsequent marriage to, a lady known variously as the 'Widow wachauf', 'El Witcho', and other things even less flattering and certainly unprintable.

Even before the ceremony, two of the founding disciples were so incensed that they took a full-page ad in the *Picaroon-Statesman* denouncing Brother Buck for betraying the most sacred of the sect's principles. They were summoned before a hastily formed ecclesiastic court and formally excommunicated.

Things got worse. On the night of his wedding, literally on the nuptial couch, Blessed Brother Buck was summoned to sing in that great choir in the sky. Although the official report of the New Orleans coroner's office clearly stated that 'the deceased, the Rev. [sic] Baxter Wilson expired of coronary failure, most probably brought on by overexertion,' the cry of 'witchcraft' immediately went up from the laity, and even from three of the remaining founding disciples.

There was talk of burning the newly widowed Mrs. Wilson at the stake. But cooler heads, led by Mr. de Wilde, prevailed. It had come to him, he announced, that Blessed Brother Buck had made the greatest sacrifice of all – marriage to a woman – to prove his devotion to the principle that the GILIAFCC, Inc., was indeed open to all kinds of people, even the heterosexual kind.

After some heated debate and just a little hair-pulling, the founding disciples announced that not only was the Widow Wilson *not* a witch, but was in fact an instrument of the Divine. A delegation of founding disciples called upon the Widow Wilson that very night to offer her a position high in the hierarchy of the GILIAFCC, Inc. She was from that night to be their Reverend Mother Emeritus.

Subsequent events, starting almost immediately, proved the wisdom of that decision. Even before the Reverend Mother Emeritus had been fitted into her newly designed vestments, the problem of how to properly plant Blessed Brother Buck was solved.

Boris Alexandrovich Korsky-Rimsakov, the world's greatest opera singer, arrived by chartered jet from Paris to console the lady he touchingly described as 'my ol' army buddy' in her hour of sorrow. He was prevailed upon to sing at the funeral, and at a memorial service held later at the New Orleans Centre for the Performing Arts. The revenue from ticket sales was more than sufficient to provide a solid bronze casket and a Canberra marble mausoleum for Buck in New Orleans' most prestigious cemetery. The mausoleum itself was later topped with a marble statue of Blessed Brother Buck pictured as St. George at the moment he slew the dragon.

(It was, to be sure, necessary to have some 'additional work' done on the statue after it was pointed out that the dragon bore an unfortunate resemblance to the Reverend Mother Emeritus. The founding disciple responsible for dealing with the sculptor was, following another ecclesiastical trial, excommunicated, but later, after a public recanting of error, he was accepted back into the fold.)

The Reverend Mother Emeritus herself, first thought of as nothing more than a figurehead, soon brought disorder out of the chaos of the business and financial affairs of the GILIAFCC, Inc.

'You can't spend twenty years as an army nurse,' as she herself said, 'without learning how to straighten things out.'

Unofficially, the Reverend Mother Emeritus also soon began to provide a broad female bosom on which the members of the congregation could rest their tearful heads and confess their innermost thoughts.

With the Reverend Mother Emeritus' firm hand on the rudder, the GILIAFCC, Inc., prospered. Branch temples were opened in suburban New Orleans, San Francisco, Chicago, and Terre Haute, Indiana. An International Headquarters Building was erected on St. Anne Street, overlooking Jackson Square and the St. Louis Cathedral.

After two years of stewardship, however, the Reverend Mother announced that she felt God wanted her back into medicine. As various plans were being discussed, a fortunate set of circumstances solved the problem. With a substantial bequest from the American Tonsil, Adenoid & Vas Deferens Society, the Ms. Prudence MacDonald Memorial School of Nursing was established. The Reverend Mother Emeritus (who was, after all, Lt. Col., Army Nurse Corps, Retired) was ideally qualified to serve as both chief of nursing instruction and house mother, and was appointed to the post. She divided her time equally between the two responsibilities. . . .

Standing impatiently inside the plate glass doors of International Headquarters, Jimmy de Wilde finally sighed with mixed relief and exasperation. The Reverend Mother Emeritus was arriving at last. But she was arriving in the Confederate grey Cadillac limousine of her most persistent suitor — Col. Beauregard C. Beaucoupmots, publisher of the *Picaroon-Statesman*.

Not only was the colonel shamelessly bent on taking the

Reverend Mother Emeritus to bride (or, as he put it, 'away from all those fruitcakes') he had learned of the Reverend Mother Emeritus' one eensy-weensy imperfection — a fondness for the grape — and exploited it whenever and wherever he could.

The limousine glided to a halt. The chauffeur rushed around the front of the car to open the door. The Reverend Mother Emeritus emerged. She was wearing a dress of light pink (Jimmy de Wilde recognised the colour as 'Tutti-frutti Rouge') that began six inches beneath her chin and ended six inches above her knees.

Over it, she wore an ankle-length mink coat, a little birthday present from the colonel. The only symbol of her religious affiliation was an eight-inch gold cross suspended around her neck and supported by her ample bosom; on it, spelled out in diamonds, were the words 'MOTHER' (on the horizontal portion) and 'EMERITUS' (on the vertical).

She held a large-sized brandy snifter in her hand. She sipped at it, then raised both hands above her head, her arms spread wide.

'Bless you, Brother Jimmy!' she said enthusiastically. 'Have you been a good boy while Reverend Mother's been away?'

'I see you're with *him* again, Reverend Mother,' Jimmy de Wilde said in a pronounced fit of pique.

'The Colonel was good enough to meet me at the airport,' The Reverend Mother Emeritus said. 'Say "Hello Jimmy," like a good boy, Beauregard!'

Beauregard said nothing. The Reverend Mother Emeritus bent and looked into the car, giving Jimmy de Wilde just cause to worry that her mammiform protuberances were about to escape their fragile binding.

Colonel Beauregard C. Beaucoupmots was resting, his mouth ajar, against the plush upholstery of his limousine. His eyes were closed and he was snoring quietly.

'Oh, Beauregard!' the Reverend Mother Emeritus said. 'I don't know what I'm going to do with you!'

'How about mercy-killing?' Jimmy de Wilde asked.

'Luther,' the Reverend Mother Emeritus said to the chauffeur, 'will you take care of the colonel? Duty calls, I'm afraid.'

'Yes, ma'am,' the chauffeur said.

'Hand me that brandy bottle,' the Reverend Mother Emeritus said. 'The colonel won't be needing it for a while, and it's been a long, long trip.'

She swept into the International Headquarters Building with Jimmy de Wilde skipping along in her wake.

'And how was Las Vegas?' Jimmy de Wilde asked.

'Brother Chester is doing splendidly,' she said. 'When I see what an effective evangelist he is, I'm just sick to think of all the years he wasted clipping poodles. Did I tell you he got the entire membership of Local 135, International Brotherhood of Hotel Front Desk Clerks, at one fell swoop? We had a lovely mass baptism in the Pool of the Vestal Virgins at Nero's Villa.'

'Anything else?' Jimmy de Wilde asked.

'I wouldn't want it to get around, Jimmy,' she said, 'but Mother Emeritus made a killing at the 21 tables.' She dipped into her purse and came out with a wad of hundred-dollar bills, which she fanned for his edification. 'More than enough, Jimmy, to get the Ms. Prudence MacDonald Memorial School of Nursing out of the red.' She smiled at him. 'To coin a phrase, Jimmy, when Reverend Mother is hot, she's hot!' She tossed the money to him. He tossed it back.

'They don't need it,' he said.

'What do you mean, they don't *need* it?' she asked. 'When I left for Vegas, the larder was bare.'

'That awful de la Chevaux person was here,' Jimmy said.

'Horsey was here?' the Reverend Mother Emeritus said. 'What did he want?' Horsey de la Chevaux normally gave the GILIAFCC, Inc., as wide a berth as he gave the Women's Christian Temperance Union and other such Protestant insanities.

54

'Horsey and the ugly ape, that terrible François Mulligan person,' Jimmy said. 'They came to apologise.'

'For what?'

'For what happened to Brother Duane.'

'What *happened* to Brother Duane?' she asked suspiciously.

'They were beastly to him, Reverend Mother,' Jimmy said. 'They shaved off all his hair – with a dull knife – and then they set him adrift in the Gulf of Mexico, *miles and miles* from shore, in a lifeboat.'

'Why?'

'I have *no* idea,' Jimmy said innocently.

'Then what was Brother Duane *doing* out miles and miles from shore in the Gulf of Mexico?' the Reverend Mother Emeritus asked. But even as she spoke, realisation dawned. 'Jimmy, you know what I've said about you fellows going out to those offshore drilling platforms!'

'They sent a helicopter for him,' Jimmy said. 'He didn't just swim out.'

'Tell Mother Emeritus *all*, Jimmy,' she said, with more than a hint of menace in her tone.

'All the ad in the *Picaroon-Statesman* said was that Chevaux Drilling Platform number seventy-eight needed people to work in their massage parlour. It didn't say anything at all about the people having to be girls.'

'But what happened when they came to pick up Brother Duane?' she asked. 'Couldn't they tell – *Jimmy*, did Brother Duane go out to the drilling platform in drag?'

'He looked *gorgeous!*' Jimmy said. 'They should have taken that into consideration. He was trying to please, for heaven's sake!'

'How badly did they hurt him?'

'Well, they cut off all his hair, as I said. And you know how he just *works* and *works* to have a lovely head of hair. And, before the Coast Guard found him floating around out there in his birthday suit, he got a very nasty sunburn.'

'Well, you were both wrong,' the Reverend Mother Emeritus said. 'You should have known better than to let Brother Duane do something like that, Jimmy. And the Knights should have simply asked him to leave. . . . How did they find out, by the way, if he looked so gorgeous?'

'How do you *think*, Reverend Mother, if I may be so bold?'

'You're both in the wrong!' she said, blushing ever so slightly.

'That awful de la Chevaux person didn't think so,' Jimmy said, a trifle righteously. He took a cheque from his back pocket and waved it at the Reverend Mother Emeritus. 'That should feed the girls for quite a while,' he said. 'Even considering their somewhat revolting capacity for food.'

'Under the circumstances,' the Reverend Mother said, 'I will have a word with Brother Duane. . . . Where is he, by the way?'

'In his room,' Jimmy said. 'He says he's not coming out until his hair grows back in.'

'Call up Wild and Wonderful Wigs,' the Reverend Mother said, 'and ask them to send someone over. Let Brother Duane have whatever he wants, and deposit the rest of the cheque to the nursing school's account.'

'Oh, Reverend Mother!' Jimmy de Wilde said. 'You have the wisdom of Solomon.'

'Solomon who?' the Reverend Mother inquired.

'Oh, never mind,' he said. 'But now that that's over, there's something else.'

'Oh?'

'Would you believe two scholarships, from income?'

'What are you talking about?'

'I don't know what all the details are, Reverend Mother, but the bottom line is that some Cubans in Miami — who must be delightfully loaded, financially speaking, of course — are going to present the nursing school with an endowment to set up the Doctors Pierce and McIntyre Memorial Scholarships.'

'Tell me more,' she said.

'All I really know is that they sent a cheque for twenty thousand dollars, to show good faith, together with a letter saying that as soon as we send them some cost figures – how much it costs per student nurse from the day she enters until the day she graduates – they'll give us the rest.'

'How interesting!'

'May I suggest, Reverend Mother, that we come up with the figures just as soon as we can? I'd like to send them to Miami before they change their minds.'

'Send them? Jimmy,' the Reverend Mother Emeritus said, 'I wouldn't think of *sending* the figures. I'll *take* them to Miami *myself*.'

'Do you think that's a good idea?' he asked.

'I think it's a splendid idea,' she said. 'If their offer is on the up and up, it seems to me that the least we can do is make them honorary disciples of the God Is Love in All Forms Christian Church, Inc., and present them with a suitably inscribed holy relic.'*

Jimmy de Wilde suspected that the Reverend Mother Emeritus was being carried away either with enthusiasm or on the wings of the brandy she had shared with Col. Beaucoupmots, but he said nothing. His long experience with the Reverend Mother Emeritus had convinced him that she generally knew what she was doing.

'As a matter of fact,' the Reverend Mother said, 'I'll take Prudence with me. She's been married to Ace long enough now to be entitled to a separate vacation. And I'm sure these

---

*It had been, for some time, the custom of the GILIAFCC, Inc., to present to people who had done some service to the GILIAFCC, Inc., a miniature replica of the mausoleum and statue of Blessed Brother Buck. The statues were carved from marble left over from the actual mausoleum and statue, and were highly valued by most recipients. The archbishop of New Orleans, for example, had been so touched by *his* holy relic that he had immediately sent it to the Vatican Museum, where today it occupies a special place in that portion of the museum devoted to pornography and pagan art.

Cubans, whoever they are, would like to see Prudence in the flesh.'

'There's no accounting for tastes, I suppose,' Jimmy de Wilde replied.

CHAPTER SIX

Walter Kosciusko Waldowski, Doctor of Dental Surgery and one-time Captain, Dental Corps, U.S. Army Reserve, sat, his totally bald skull gleaming in the reflected light from the chandeliers, in the bar of the Ritz Hotel on Place Vendôme, in Paris, France, staring into his sixth beer and ruminating on the injustice of life.

He had done, he knew, all that could reasonably be expected of a husband, father, and dental surgeon. When Wanda Waldowski, his only child, a comely blonde of nineteen, had returned from the University of Michigan to their Hamtramck home, heart-broken, her spirit crushed by the termination of her engagement, he had not only offered her his broad fatherly shoulder, but had agreed with his wife, Wilma, that what the child needed was a change of scenery, something to take her mind off her romantic tragedy.

He had, at the time, thought this would mean that Wilma and Wanda would drive to Chicago and spend a lot of money shopping. He had had no idea that the change of scene they'd had in mind was two weeks in Gay Paree. But even when that announcement had been made, he had gritted his teeth and forced a smile. Two weeks in Gay Paree obviously meant two weeks away from his dental practice, and, more important, from the South Hamtramck Polish-American Social and Civic Betterment Club, where Dr. Waldowski operated and participated in the longest running seven-card stud poker game in the history of Hamtramck (or, for that matter, in the history of Poles in America) — but for his daughter's sake, he would go to Gay Paree.

He had, without complaint, taken seven different tours of Paris, all of them quite cultural and educational and of absolutely no interest to him whatever. Wanda seemed to be perking up a little, and he was willing to pay any price necessary to see her smile again. . . .

Dr. Waldowski's initial reaction to the shattered engagement had been a very strong urge to go to the university, invade the football dormitory, and choke to death the defensive tackle who had toyed with Wanda's affections. He had been dissuaded from this notion by his wife, who had said that it would be unseemly conduct for a dental surgeon who had, as the bottom line, a daughter to marry off. Certainly, Wilma had pointed out, no respectable family would be willing to see their son married to the daughter of a choker of defensive tackles.

Dr. Waldowski had reacted with nothing more than a wince when he'd seen the bills for the clothing his Wilma had bought their Wanda to take her mind off her tragic loss. He had left Hamtramck; he had come to Gay Paree.

And then, yesterday, he had made the supreme sacrifice – he had agreed to take wife and daughter to the opera. His interest in grand opera was on a par with his interest in the moral pronouncements of politicians; if at all possible, he would rather not hear either.

Butfor Wanda, he had been prepared to make even this sacrifice. He would get tickets to the opera, he told his wife and daughter, and he would put on what he referred to as his 'boiled shirt and waiter's jacket,' and he would silently undergo the experience, without one word of complaint.

'And awake, Walter,' Wilma had said. 'Wide awake.'

'Sitting on the edge of my seat, Wilma dear, with a smile on my lips,' he had assured her. 'Anything to take Wanda's mind off you-know-what.'

There was only one small problem. There were no tickets to the opera available. This was one problem Dr. Waldowski hadn't considered. He had thought that it was 5-2 that he could come by tickets the way he normally came by tickets – that is to say, by flipping a coin, double or nothing, with the ticket seller. If that failed, he would have to buy tickets the way ordinary people, those without sporting blood, did; in other words, to buy them at face value. Dr. Waldowski hadn't been able to imagine a situation in which an opera performance would be sold out. It wasn't, after all, generally speaking, a contact sport. But even in that eventuality, he'd believed that he'd be able to deal with a ticket scalper. Ticket scalpers, as a rule, had a little sporting blood, and that would bring him back to flipping a coin, double or nothing, and reopen the possibility that he could come by three tickets free of charge.

With that in mind, he had gone to the Hotel Ritz's concierge and told him he wanted three of the best seats in the house for that night's performance at the Paris Opera.

'Zat,' the concierge, a formidable gentleman, had said, 'is ab-zo-lutely out of zee question, M'sieu.'

'It's M'sieu le Doctor to you, Jack,' Walter had replied. 'And what do you mean, out of the question?'

'Tonight, M'sieu le Docteur,' the concierge had said, 'zere is zee *performance magnifique.*'

'I don't care what the opera is, Jack, just get me three tickets.'

'Out of zee question, M'sieu le Docteur,' the concierge had said, with what Walter had thought was barely disguised delight. 'I have said zat already. I will say it again. Tonight is a *performance magnifique.*'

'What the hell is a *performance magnifique*?'

'Tickets for a *performance magnifique*, M'sieu le Docteur, are twice as much money as tickets to a *performance ordinaire.*'

'O.K.,' Dr. Waldowski had said, taking out his sheaf of traveller's cheques, noting that the sheaf was much thinner than it had been, and ripping off two cheques. 'How much? As we say in South Hamtramck, you've got me by the short hairs.'

The concierge had thrown up his hands in exasperation. 'M'sieu doesn't understand me! Perhaps m'sieu is not too bright. One more time. Zair *are no tickets.* Period.'

'You mean they have a full house?' Walter Waldowski had asked in disbelief.

'When *Cher* Boris sings, M'sieu, zair is always zee full house.'

'What, or who, is *Cher* Boris?'

'M'sieu has nevair heard of Boris Alexandrovich Korsky-Rimsakov?'

'You got it, Jack,' Walter Waldowski had said.

'M'sieu will permit me to say zat I am *un*-surprised,' the concierge had said. 'And permit me a small word of advice. When zee concierge of zee Ritz says zair *are* no tickets for a *performance magnifique*, m'sieu would do well to believe zat zair are *no* tickets.'

And with that, flapping the tails of his frock coat, the concierge had walked away.

In the somewhat naïve belief that the American Embassy had been established in Paris to cater to the pressing needs of American taxpayers, Dr. Waldowski had then summoned a taxicab and ordered that he be taken to the embassy.

That had been a difficult experience. For one thing, the embassy had been entertaining at an afternoon *thé dansant et les cocktails* staff members of other embassies, and as the third assistant deputy under-secretary for tourist relations to whom Dr. Waldowski had finally gotten to speak had said, 'Under those circumstances, it's really bad form for a lousy civilian like you to come here at all, you know.'

After Dr. Waldowski had caught his attention by grabbing him by his Sulka necktie and suspending him two feet off the ground, however, the third assistant deputy under-secretary had been good enough to explain the circumstances.

The man to whom the Ritz concierge had referred as '*Cher* Boris' was Boris Alexandrovich Korsky-Rimsakov, who four years before had been declared a National Treasure of the French Republic. He was the world's greatest opera singer.

'I thought Caruso was the best,' Dr. Waldowski had said.

'Caruso has, I believe, gone to the Great Opera House in the Sky,' the third assistant deputy under-secretary for tourist relations had replied. 'The point is that tickets for a *performance magnifique*, which is any performance at which Maestro Korsky-Rimsakov sings, are quite impossible to obtain. I, myself, have never heard him sing, and we diplomats, you know, are much more important than you lousy taxpayers.'

'I demand to see the ambassador,' Dr. Waldowski had said.

'Oh, that's quite impossible, I'm afraid. We have strict instructions to keep you tourists away from him.'

Four very large Marines had seen Dr. Waldowski to the door and through the gate.

'You haven't heard the end of this?' Dr. Waldowski had cried. 'I'm a personal friend of Mayor Daley!' But he knew it was a hollow threat even before the Marine replied.

'He was here last week. He told us he was a personal friend of the Secretary of State when we threw him out. . . .'

Afraid to face Wilma's wrath, Dr. Waldowski had assured her that everything was in order.

'It had better be,' she'd said with one of her sweet little smiles. 'I just found out that *Cher* Boris is going to sing. The girls in Hamtramck will be simply *green* when they hear I heard him sing in the flesh.'

'You know this *Cher* Boris guy, huh?'

'Doesn't every woman?' Wilma had breathed. Dr. Waldowski hadn't seen that look in her eyes since the day they were married.

'Wilma, darling,' he had said, 'I'm going down to the lobby to check on the car.'

'Stay out of the bar, Walter, darling,' Wilma had said, with another of her sweet little smiles.

'Of course, my love,' Dr. Waldowski had replied.

Suddenly, there had been a burst of inspiration. He had walked out of the front door of the Ritz and set off at a dead run for the American Express Building on Rue Sphinx. When he'd first arrived in Paris, he had been accosted by a distinguished-looking gentleman standing outside this building who had offered to sell him postcards, and (this accom-

63

panied by a leer) 'just about anything else you might want in Paris.'

Dr. Waldowski's heart had beat a little faster as he'd reached the building and seen the man standing there. He ripped out a couple more traveller's cheques.

'Is that offer of yours to get me anything I want in Paris still good?' he'd begun.

'For a price, M'sieu,' the man had replied. 'Anything.'

'Great,' Waldowski had said. 'Three tickets to the opera. Price no object.'

The man had laughed at him, practically doubling over with uncontrolled hilarity.

Dr. Waldowski had slunk back to the Ritz, and, forgetting Wilma's stern injunction, headed straight for the bar.

For five beers, he'd sat staring at the bubbles with nary a thought of how he could get out of his predicament. Halfway through beer six, however, there was a faint light at the end of the dark tunnel. He would get lost.

This was a strange city. Getting lost was something that happened to people in strange cities. Far better that Wilma darling mock him for getting lost than find out that not only had he not been able to get three lousy tickets for a lousy opera, he had lied about it. She might, he reasoned desperately, even be glad that he was no longer lost.

'What do I owe you, Charley?' he demanded of the bartender.

'Three hundred francs,' the bartender replied with hauteur. 'In your devalued American currency, which I will accept only because I have a big heart, that's twelve dollars — with tax, fifteen.'

'Fifteen dollars for six lousy beers?'

'It breaks down to two-fifty a glass, M'sieu, and we have, of course, thrown in the peanuts free of charge.'

Dr. Waldowski paid the bill, walked quickly through the lobby, and turned left. Two blocks down the street, he looked up and saw the Opera building itself leering at him across the Place de l'Opera. He turned down the next alley, which happened to be Rue Danou; it was dark and looked like an entirely satisfactory street on which to become lost.

This initial gut reaction was almost immediately confirmed when he passed a set of swinging doors, around which oozed the smell of draft beer, hot dogs, and sauerkraut. He spun on his heels and pushed open the swinging doors.

It was a saloon virtually identical to a hundred saloons back home in Hamtramck, and somehow it had miraculously been transported all the way to Paris, France. There were even a waiter and a Shriner, in full regalia, drinking and having hot dogs at the bar.

'What can I do for you, Mac?' the bartender snarled in American. Dr. Waldowski, who had expected to be greeted by one more arrogant Frenchman, wondered if he was dreaming or losing his mind. He realised it didn't matter. Whatever the explanation, he wasn't going to rock the boat.

'Boilermaker and a redhot,' he ordered. 'And see what the guys at the end of the bar will have.'

The bartender delivered the hot dog and drink to Dr. Waldowski, and then delivered what they wanted to the guys at the end of the bar. The waiter (Dr. Waldowski could tell he was a waiter because he was wearing the same black jacket with velvet lapels and bow tie that *he* was wearing) raised the beer glass to him, smiled, and drained it. He had a word with the bartender, and, in a moment, a foaming glass of beer came sliding down the bar. The beer stopped precisely in front of Dr. Waldowski.

'Live today, for tomorrow we die,' Dr. Waldowski philosophised, raising the beer glass and draining it and then signalling to the bartender to send another one down the bar.

The waiter, instead of drinking the beer, picked it up and walked down the bar to Dr. Waldowski.

'T. Mullins Yancey,' he said. 'Always a pleasure to meet a fellow beer drinker.'

'Walter ... they call me Walt ... Waldowski,' Dr.

65

Waldowski said. They shook hands. Dr. Waldowski raised his beer glass and drained it. 'Mud in your eye, T. Mullins,' he said.

'Mud in *your* eye, Walt,' T. Mullins Yancey replied, raising his glass and draining it. 'I'm really glad to meet you, Walt,' he said. 'There's nothing worse than trying to drink beer with a total teetotal, if you know what I mean.'

'You mean your Shriner friend's on the wagon?'

'Nothing but orange juice,' T. Mullins replied, as the Shriner, adjusting his ornate headdress, slipped off the barstool and started down the bar. Waldowski saw that he was a little guy, not more than five-five, and had a dark skin.

'Give us a couple more, Eddie,' T. Mullins Yancey said to the bartender, 'and another orange juice for the prince.'

'Good evening,' Waldowski said.

'Prince, say hello to Walt. Walt, shake hands with the prince.'

'How are you, Prince?' Waldowski said. 'My Cousin Mable married a Protestant, and he's a Shriner.'

'How interesting,' Prince said.

'Yeah,' Walt Waldowski said. 'I'm K. of C., myself, but I always admired the Shriners.'

'As it happens,' Prince said, brightening, 'I am an honorary member of the Knights of Columbus.' Walter Waldowski had never heard of any honorary Knights of Columbus, and was surprised when the man flashed a genuine-looking K. of C. membership card issued by Sub-consistory Number Eighteen of some Deep South Consistory. (His eyes, truth to tell, were not focusing too well at the time.)

'It's always a pleasure to meet a fellow Knight,' Waldowski said. 'Bartender, two more boilermakers and a glass of whatever my brother Knight is having.'

'What brings you to Paris, Walt?'

'I'm here with the wife and daughter,' Waldowski replied. 'You?'

'I'd rather not talk about it,' T. Mullins Yancey said. 'I'm working.'

'Yeah, I suppose it is a tough racket,' Waldowski said. 'I'm a dentist, myself.'

'Is that so?'

'I'd rather not talk about it,' Waldowski said.

'I'll drink to that,' T. Mullins Yancey said. 'Two more boilermakers, Charley.'

'No more for me.' the prince said. 'I'm up to my ears in fruit juice.'

'You're a real drag, Prince, you know that?' T. Mullins Yancey said.

'If you insist,' the prince said.

'Maybe you thought I was a waiter, too,' Waldowski said. 'The way I'm dressed and all. But I'm not. The reason I'm dressed up like this is because I'm supposed to go to the opera.'

'I'd rather not talk about the opera, either,' T. Mullins Yancey said. 'I'm as full up with the opera as the prince is with orange juice.'

That brilliant riposte naturally called for another boilermaker.

'I know why *I* don't like the opera,' T. Mullins Yancey said. 'But what have you got against it?'

'It's not so much what I've got against it, as what my wife is going to do to me when she finds out I can't get tickets for it like I promised.'

'She should have known that getting tickets for a *performance magnifique* was too much to ask,' T. Mullins Yancey said.

'What's with this *Cher* Boris guy?' Dr. Waldowski asked.

'Don't ask,' T. Mullins Yancey replied. 'You wouldn't like the answer.'

'In that case, I won't ask,' Dr. Waldowski said, going along. He changed the subject. 'You here in Paris on some sort of Shriner's convention, Prince?'

'I beg your pardon?'

'He lives here,' T. Mullins Yancey answered for him.

'I didn't know that the Shrine had temples in Europe,' Dr. Waldowski said.

'What is he talking about?' the prince asked.

'You wouldn't understand, Prince,' T. Mullins Yancey said. 'Shut up and drink your orange juice.' He returned his attention to Dr. Waldowski. 'You say the little woman is going to blow up when she finds out you don't have tickets?'

'That, T. Mullins, old buddy, is the understatement of the year,' Dr. Waldowski confessed.

At that point, as if on cue, the swinging doors to Harry's New York Bar swung open and Mrs. Wilma Waldowski, accompanied by Miss Wanda Waldowski, both attired in brand-new and rather attractive evening dresses, swept in.

'Ah ha!' Mrs. Waldowski cried. 'The concierge was right. I couldn't believe you capable of such perfidy, but the concierge laid me three to seven that I could find you in this transplanted saloon, and he was right!'

'Papa dear, how could you?' Wanda Waldowski asked. 'With me in my present heart-broken condition?'

'Hello, Wilma, darling,' Dr. Waldowski replied somewhat weakly.

'Don't you "Wilma darling" me, you Polish snake in the grass,' Wilma darling said. 'When we get to the opera, everyone will know, everyone will *smell*, that you've spent the afternoon and early evening with your snout in a beer mug.'

'About the opera, Wilma, darling,' Dr. Waldowski began.

'What *about* the opera?' Wilma darling demanded. 'You haven't lost the tickets, have you?'

'Not exactly,' Dr. Waldowski said.

'What do you mean, "not exactly"?'

Dr. Waldowski took a deep breath. 'The truth of the matter, Wilma, darling –' he began.

Wilma darling picked up a two-gallon container of dill pickles from the bar and held it above her head as she awaited his answer. Dr. Waldowski, always the optimist, thought things could be worse. The two-gallon jar of pickles and pickle juice was only half full.

'Go on,' Wilma said. 'Explain yourself, you pulicose* Polack — while you still have the ability!'

*Mrs. Wilma Waldowski, then Miss Wilma Q. Kelly, had won the Greater Chicago Area Ninth-Grade Spelling Contest by correctly spelling 'pulicose' (pu-li-cose, from the Latin *pulicosis*, adj.: infested with fleas). She had thereafter, perhaps in a subconscious attempt to regain her moment of glory, often injected the word into her conversation, most often when discussing her husband.

CHAPTER SEVEN

'Walter,' T. Mullins Yancey said, 'you said she was beautiful, but you didn't tell me that she's nothing but a child bride.'

Wilma Waldowski looked at T. Mullins Yancey with suspicion in her eyes, but she did not throw the pickle jar still poised over her head.

'Permit me, gracious lady,' T. Mullins Yancey said, 'The great privilege of introducing myself. I am Theosophilus Mullins Yancey. *Doctor* T. Mullins Yancey.'

'I've been married to this procine Polish tooth-jerker long enough to know how you molar mechanics stick together,' Mrs. Waldowski said. 'You can stop wasting your hot air on me, Curly. I've got your number.'

'Madame, I assure you that I am not a member of the dental profession,' T. Mullins Yancey replied.

'What are you, then, some kind of quack?'

'I am a doctor of medicine, dear lady,' T. Mullins Yancey replied.

'M.D.?' she asked in disbelief.

'M.D., Ph.D., D.D., and D.V.M.,' he replied modestly, extending his card.

It was necessary, of course, for Mrs. Waldowski to put down the pickle jar in order to take Yancey's card, which she did. Walter Waldowski let out his breath. Mrs. Waldowski examined the card.

THE T. MULLINS YANCEY FOUNDATION
Manhattan, Kansas

Theosophilus Mullins Yancey
M.D., Ph.D., D.D., and D.V.M.
Chief of Staff

'Doctor,' Wilma Waldowski said, oozing feminine charm from every pore, 'whatever must you think of little me?'

'Only that you must have brought beauty and joy beyond measure into Walter's otherwise drab life,' T. Mullins Yancey said.

'Yes,' Mrs. Waldowski purred. 'How discerning you are, Doctor!'

'He was talking of nothing but you, dear lady,' T. Mullins went on, 'telling us how much you appreciated the opera, and *Cher* Boris in particular, and how happy he was, as a small token of his boundless gratitude to you for sharing his drab and miserable life, to have been able to obtain the president's ... formerly the Emperor Napoleon's ... box for you and your lovely daughter.'

'Walter did *what*?' Wilma darling asked.

'What did I do?' Dr. Waldowski asked.

'We were, at the very instant you and your charming daughter entered, like dual rays of sunshine, this dark hole to which we repaired in desperation when the limousine broke down, about to come for you,' Dr. Yancey went on.

'What limousine?' Wilma Waldowski asked, mixed awe and suspicion in her voice.

'Tell her what limousine, Prince,' Dr. Yancey said. Then, before Prince could open his mouth: 'Oh, forgive me, forgive me! Mrs. Waldowski, Miss Waldowski, may I present His Royal Highness Prince Hassan ad Kayam, Ambassador Extraordinary and Plenipotentiary of the Sheikhdom of Hussid to the French Republic?'

'Charmed,' the prince said, bowing as he kissed Mrs. Waldowski's hand.

'Walter,' Mrs. Waldowski said to her companion on the march down life's rocky road, 'I'm *sure* there will be a limousine outside, and that this isn't one of your clever little deceptions.'

'You're going to the opera with us, Your Royal Princeship?' Miss Wanda Waldowski asked.

'Your father has, as one more manifestation of his all-around generosity,' Dr. Yancey said, 'very graciously has asked His Highness and myself to join you. Unless, of course, you would rather that we didn't?'

'Of course you will,' Mrs. Waldowski said. 'Any friends of my beloved Walter are friends of mine.'

Dr. Yancey looked a bit disappointed, but smiled bravely.

'See if the car is out there, Prince,' he said. 'Walter and I are going to have another little libation.'

'A drink?' Mrs. Waldowski asked, suspicion returning.

'It is an old Parisian custom, Mrs. Waldowski,' Dr. Yancey said, 'dating back to the days of Napoleon, in whose box you are about to sit. It's called "*une pour le route.*" You *do* speak French, of course?'

'I'm afraid not,' Mrs. Waldowski confessed.

'*Encore une fois,*' Dr. Yancey said to the bartender.

'Isn't that odd?' Mrs. Waldowski said as the drinks were delivered. 'If I didn't know better, if we weren't in Paris, I'd say they looked like boilermakers.'

'Would you?' Dr. Yancey replied. He drained his in two gulps. 'Allons, *mes enfants,*' he said, '*à l'opera!*'

'This is,' Mrs. Wilma Waldowski said to her spouse, 'what I believe is known as the moment of truth.'

Dr. and Mrs. Waldowski and their daughter, Wanda, were quite surprised to find waiting outside the swinging doors of Harry's New York Bar ('Just tell the cab-driver sank Roo Dan-oo') the promised limousine. It was a Cadillac, bearing on its rear doors in gold the coat of arms of the Sheikhdom of Hussid.*

---

*The Royal Coat of Arms of the Sheikhdom of Hussid consisted of two crossed scimitars surmounted by an oil-well drilling rig, in turn surmounted by the dollar sign.

The gleaming front fenders of the Cadillac each bore the coat of arms on a flag. The limousine was part of a procession. Out in front were two motorcycles ridden by members of the French Gendarmerie Nationale. Behind the motorcycles were two black Citröen sedans each flying the flag of Hussid and filled with His Royal Highness' bodyguards; these were dressed in flowing robes and armed with silver-plated sub-machine guns. A third Citröen also filled with bodyguards brought up the rear.

As soon as the limousine door closed on Mrs. Waldowski, the sirens of the motorcycle escort began to wail, and the convoy moved out of Rue Danou. It turned right on Rue de Rivoli, toward the Opera. Gendarmes on duty in the Place de l'Opéra furiously blew their whistles, twirled their capes, gestured menacingly with their batons, and finally stopped all traffic passing through the Place de l'Opéra and made room for the convoy to swoop up to the main entrance to the Opera.

The general manager of the opera came bounding down the stairs between rows of ornately uniformed troopers of the Garde Républicain to personally open the door himself.

'I'm so glad you're here, Doctor,' he said. 'The maestro, *Cher* Boris, refuses to sing unless you're in the audience.'

Mrs. Waldowski looked suspicious again, and Dr. Yancey saw this.

'You've got that wrong,' he said. 'He simply didn't want to begin until he was sure that his good friend Dr. Waldowski and his charming and beautiful wife and daughter were in the audience. If you will show the ladies to the Emperor's Box, Dr. Waldowski and I will drop in on the maestro.'

'Walter, did he say that you *know* Boris Alexandrovich Korsky-Rimsakov?' Mrs. Waldowski demanded.

'That was Walter's little surprise,' Dr. Yancey said. 'He was saving that for last.' He grabbed Waldowski by the arm and propelled him into the opera house. Mrs. Waldowski, her mouth open, allowed herself to be led up the stairs.

The Sheikhdom of Hussid provided thirty-eight percent of the petroleum needs of the Republic of France. For that reason alone the Hussidic ambassador would be granted every courtesy at the disposal of the French government, but the relationship had been made even warmer by the connection between Air Hussid and the French aviation industry. Air Hussid was the only airline in the world to have purchased the droop-nosed supersonic transport aircraft Le Discorde designed and built by the French. Only Air Hussid, which was funded by petty cash from the Hussidic Royal Exchequer, and thus not forced to consider such mundane things as the cost-per-seat-per-mile ($2.07), could afford it.

73

Dr. Waldowski was in that bemused state that sometimes comes upon people who have, in the words of Mrs. Waldowski, 'spent the afternoon and early evening with the snout in a beer mug.' He allowed himself to be led, without protest, past a door guarded by gendarmes into the dressing-room area of the Opera. Two more, very large, policemen guarded another door, on which was painted a large gold star, the words BORIS ALEX-ANDROVICH KORSKY-RIMSAKOV, and, in somewhat smaller letters, UN TROVE OFFICIEL DE LA REPUBLIC DE FRANCE.

From behind the closed door came a very loud voice.

'I'm not going to sing unless Dr. Yancey is in the audience!' it said. 'Can't you get it through your thick Frog head that we are engaged in a medical experiment of the greatest importance?'

'I see the foghorn's in his usual good mood,' Dr. Yancey said to Dr. Waldowski as he walked past the policemen and pushed open the door.

'Well, there he is,' the occupant of the room said. 'No fault of yours.'

Dr. Waldowski saw a very large (six-five, three-hundred-pound) bearded male human being reclining on a chaise longue. He was attired in the costume of Benvenuto Cellini and was sipping casually from the neck of an enormous bottle of champagne.

'I am glad to see you, of course, Doctor,' Boris Alexandro-vich Korsky-Rimsakov said. 'And, as a fellow genius, I understand, of course, your odd behaviour. But who is this fat bald man in the rented tuxedo, and how dare you bring him to my dressing-room?'

'He is a friend of mine, and he has a problem,' Dr. Yancey said. 'How much of the bubbly have you had, Boris?'

'I just this moment cracked the second bottle,' Boris said. He looked at Dr. Waldowski. 'Fat, bald man, why are you staring at my mouth?'

'Have you exercised?' Dr. Yancey asked.

'Twice,' Boris replied. 'If I sing superbly after one exercise and a glass or two of bubbly, how superbly – we may need a

74

new adjective — am I going to sing after exercising twice and having twice as much bubbly?'

'I recognize the cap on your incisor,' Dr. Waldowski said just a little thickly.

'I have warned you once, you fugitive from a Polish wedding, to stop staring at my mouth!' Boris said to Dr. Waldowski. 'What do you mean, "cap on my incisor"? Are you suggesting that I, Boris Alexandrovich Korsky-Rimsakov, whom this sainted man, this reincarnate Hippocrates, will tell you is the possessor of the finest body since Charles Atlas, have false teeth?'

'Just a cap on the incisor,' Dr. Waldowski said. 'Odd — it's mine, but I don't remember you.'

'Who is this maniac you have brought into my dressing room?' Boris asked.

Dr. Yancey shrugged his shoulders.

'Were you ever in the army?' Dr. Waldowski pursued.

'What the hell kind of an impertinent question is that?' Boris replied, getting to his feet, putting his hands on his hips, and glowering at Dr. Waldowski. 'How dare you, fat little man, come into my dressing room and ask me a question like that?'

'Well, *were* you?'

'Tell him, Doctor,' Boris said.

'He was in the army.'

'Not only was I *in* the army, skinhead,' Boris added, 'but I was very nearly as good a soldier as I am a singer. You are looking, sir, at the finest Browning automatic rifleman ever to grace the ranks of the finest regiment in the army, the 223rd Infantry,' He raised the jeroboam of champagne to his lips, drank deeply, and said, with deep emotion, 'Here's to you, my buddies, wherever you may be!'

'At Chorwon,' Dr. Waldowski said. 'In the Iron Triangle.'

'How could you possibly know that?' Boris said, fascination in his voice.

'And you were once a patient in the 4077th MASH, were you not?' Dr. Waldowski said.

'This is absolutely incredible,' Boris said. He spun on his heel, snatched another bottle of champagne from a cooler, flipped the cork out effortlessly, and handed it to Dr. Waldowski. 'You will, of course, sir, join me in a small toast to the finest medical facility ever to follow our beloved flag? I give you the 4077th MASH.'

'The 4077th MASH,' Dr. Waldowski said. 'The Good Ol' Double Natural!' They took healthy swigs from the necks of the bottles.

'How did you know about that?' Boris said, looking at him suspiciously.

'About what?'

'About it being the Double Natural. Here's to the Double Natural!' They toasted the Double Natural.

'I was *in* the Double Natural,' Dr. Waldowski said. 'That's how I know. That's where I capped your tooth.'

'You, sir,' Boris said angrily, 'are beneath contempt. You are attempting, for reasons I can't begin to understand, to represent yourself as something you are not and couldn't possibly be.'

'I'll have you know, you big ape, that I was the dental surgeon of the Double Natural MASH,' Dr. Waldowski said.

'Now I've got you, you revolting imposter!' Boris Alexandrovich Korsky-Rimsakov said. 'As it happens, I was friendly with that distinguished practitioner of the dental arts. He was a tall, slender chap with a splendid head of curly blonde hair. The only thing wrong with him was his name. He had some impossible Polack name.'

'At least I was using my own name,' Dr. Waldowski said. 'Which is more than I can say for you.'

Boris Alexandrovich Korsky-Rimsakov peered intently at Dr. Waldowski. Suddenly recognition dawned and he smiled.

'My God, old buddy, you really *have* gone to hell over the years, haven't you? You're bald and you're fat, and to judge from the cut of that waiter suit, you've been anything but a financial success. But it doesn't matter. It doesn't matter at all.' He stepped up to Dr. Waldowski, picked him up by the shoulders, kissed him wetly in the middle of the forehead, and set him back down. 'I, Boris Alexandrovich Korsky-Rimsakov, love you. Platonically speaking, of course.'

'What was that Bob Alexander business?' Dr. Waldowski said. 'I remember you as PFC Bob Alexander. You caught a piece of shrapnel in the mouth.'

'I caught, to be precise, eleven pieces of shrapnel,' Boris said. 'You can carry modesty a bit too far, you know.'

'I remember the one in the mouth because it took the tip of your incisor off,' Dr. Waldowski said. 'That's when I capped it.'

'I thought you molar mechanics had some sort of a set of ethics that's supposed to keep you from broadcasting your patients' most intimate medical secrets.'

'I hate to break this up,' Dr. Yancey said, 'but there are three thousand people out there waiting to hear you sing.'

'To hell with that,' Boris said. 'The Painless Polack and I, now that we've found each other, are going to have a couple of belts and scare up some broads, for auld lang syne.'

'Including Mrs. Waldowski and their daughter,' Dr. Yancey said.

'I suppose that does put a crimp in what seemed like such a good idea,' Boris said. 'We'll have to work something out for later. How long are you going to be in town?'

'Not long. I've got to get back for a dental convention in Miami.'

'After the performance, you will be my guests for dinner, of course. You look like you could use a good meal.' He looked around the room. 'Where's the prince? He's always underfoot, but when you need him, God knows, he's off somewhere chasing broads.'

'He's with Mrs. Waldowski in your box, Boris,' Dr. Yancey said.

'Be a good guy, Doc, and tell him to lay on a little party, will you, for afterwards? It isn't every day that I bump into an old army buddy.' He tilted the jeroboam of champagne to his lips one more time, draining it, threw the empty bottle into a wastebasket, and did two quick knee bends.

77

'I must now go sing and bring beauty into their drab lives,' he said as he swept out of the room. 'Have Dr. Yancey tell you about all the sacrifices I made for my art, Painless, while I'm gone.'

Dr. Waldowski sat down and noisily exhaled.

'What's the matter, Walt?' Dr. Yancey asked.

'That was a lot to happen all at once,' Waldowski confessed. 'A half an hour ago, I was about to be crowned with a two-gallon pickle jar for not being able to get tickets to hear the world's greatest opera singer sing, and now it turns out he's nothing more than a ex-patient.'

'You're right, of course,' Dr. Yancey said. 'I think what we need is a drink.'

'I wouldn't dare leave now.'

'Take it from me, Walt, your wife and daughter won't miss you. Once old Lion Loins gets on the stage, every other man becomes invisible.'

'You're kidding!'

'No, I'm not. That's what I'm doing in Paris. Trying to understand the phenomenon.'

'You really are a doctor, then? I thought you were just saying that to help me out with the little woman.'

'I'm really a doctor,' Yancey said. 'Tell me, Walt, did you ever read The Book?'

'The Book?' Dr. Waldowski said. 'The Book? Oh, you mean, *The* Book. *Sex and Health Through Constant Coitus?*'

'Right,' Dr. Yancey said.

'Of course, I have, T. Mullins,' Dr. Waldowski said. 'I make a real effort to keep up with the advanced thought of other branches of the healing arts.'

'And what did you think of it?' T. Mullins Yancey asked.

'Brilliant,' Dr. Waldowski said. 'Absolutely brilliant. And the companion volume, the one about exercise.* Truly monumental works.'

---

*Dr. Waldowski here referred to *Sexual Intercourse as Exercise.*

'How kind of you to say so,' Dr. Yancey said shyly.

Dr. Waldowski struck his forehead with his hand. Since he had a large forehead and a somewhat hammy hand, the sound was like that of a rifle shot. 'How stupid of me! I should have connected the names. You are *that* Dr. Yancey! The sage of Manhattan, Kansas!'

'I don't think of myself as a sage,' Dr. Yancey said. 'I was a simple family physician for a long time, and I still think of myself as one.'

'I think I will have that drink,' Dr. Waldowski said. 'This is all too much for me.'

Dr. Waldowski and Dr. Yancey left the Opera by the stage door, walked back across the Place de l'Opera to Rue de Rivoli, and then on to Rue Danou and back through the swinging doors of Harry's New York Bar.

Over boilermakers, the two exchanged both confidences and fill-in background material on Boris Alexandrovich Korsky-Rimsakov, a.k.a. PFC Bob Alexander.

'I don't mean to pry,' Dr. Waldowski said presently, 'but I've always wondered how you came to specialise in your area. I mean, I don't know of any special programme in medical school.'

'I suppose you could say I'm a pioneer,' Dr. Yancey replied. 'I mean Freud talked a lot about it. But he never recommended any treatment. He just had them lying there alone on the couch.'

'But how did you get started?' Dr. Waldowski asked.

'Well, there I was, in my little clinic in Manhattan,' Dr. Yancey began. 'It had been a rough day. All morning I'd had a stream of perfectly healthy females in to see me, complaining about vague, imaginary illnesses. I suppose when you get right down to it, if I hadn't had a couple of extra belts at lunch, I'd still be there.'

'What happened?'

'Her name was Agnes,' Dr. Yancey said. 'I remember her quite well. She'd been coming to me for about three years, regular as clockwork, complaining of vague

79

stomach distress, pain in the lower back, you know the routine.'

'I play poker with a couple of guys who run a G&O operation,' Waldowski said. 'They've cried on my shoulder a lot.'

'O.K. You know what I'm talking about. Well, as she sat there, reciting her litany of imaginary complaints, I *knew* what ailed her. Something, probably the booze, pushed me over the edge, and I told her not only what ailed her, but what to do about it.'

'What did she say?'

'She got white in the face and told me she'd never been so insulted in her life and was going to bring me up before the county medical society.'

'Did she?'

'No. She apparently thought it over. She was back in three days, smiling from ear to ear. Brought me a half-gallon of twelve-year-old Scotch and told me she was sending her sister-in-law in to see me.'

'It was as simple as that?'

'It could have gone the wrong way. I was lucky, that's all. I admit it.'

'What do you mean?'

'Well, when Charley — Agnes' husband — came home from the office and found Agnes lying on the floor in front of the fireplace wearing nothing but black mesh stockings and a mask, he at first thought she was plastered. But she was determined to go all the way — she was really desperate — and when he got on the phone to call their minister to come over and exorcise John Barleycorn, she got up and started to belly dance. That's all it took. There was nothing really wrong with Charley. He hung the phone up just as the minister came on the line. From there on in, no problem.'

'And that started the whole thing, huh?' Dr. Waldowski asked. 'The Yancey Foundation? The Joyful Practices Publishing Company? *Togetherness!* Magazine?'

'That did it,' Dr. Yancey said. 'Agnes didn't tell Charley

80

about me, and what I'd told her, until they came back from their second honeymoon.'

'What was his reaction?'

'He was grateful. Pathetically grateful. It was old Charley who really encouraged me to give up my family practice and get into sex. He said it was a gift I had no right to deny humanity.'

'He was right, of course,' Dr. Waldowski said. 'Until I put your books into my waiting room, replacing the *Reader's Digest*, my patients used to come into the chair so uptight I couldn't get them to open their mouths. But since I put your books — and *Togetherness!* Magazine, too, of course — out there, why, T. Mullins, they walk in smiling, with their mouths open. They don't even seem to know I'm working on them.'

'I like to think I do some good,' Dr. Yancey said modestly.

'You haven't told me how you came to meet Boris,' Dr. Waldowski said.

'At first, to tell you the truth, I thought I had some kind of nut on my hands,' Dr. Yancey replied. 'You know, of course, that we have that "In My Experience" column in *Togetherness!* where the readers write in and share their experiences?'

'I read it faithfully,' Dr. Waldowski said. 'I've found it very educational.'

'Well, I kept getting these . . . what shall I say? somewhat incredible pieces, unsigned, about — well, I remember one in particular called "Exercise in Pressurised Aircraft Above Thirty Thousand Feet." '

'I remember that,' Dr. Waldowski said. 'I cut it out and saved it.'

'Well, then, you know what I'm talking about. Would you believe a story like that, one man going through the entire corps de ballet of the Vienna Opera in a 747 en route to Leningrad?'

'Don't take offence, Theosophilus, ol' buddy,' Dr. Waldowski said, 'but if it weren't for the reputation of the

81

Yancey Foundation — your own impeccable reputation — I'm afraid I *wouldn't* have believed it.'

'I don't publish a thing I don't check out. I went to Vienna and checked that story myself. It was true. The girls still talk about it. Not only was it true, but it got better . . . or maybe worse. The word got around, of course, and the girls in the Leningrad Opera Ballet said it was nothing but another empty capitalistic boast.'

'So what happened?'

'Boris said that he felt it was his clear duty as a member of the John Birch Society to squelch the rumour.'

'What do you mean?'

'Boris Alexandrovich Korsky-Rimsakov is probably the only member of the John Birch Society who is also a Hero of Soviet Art and Labour,' Dr. Yancey said. 'They saved face, of course, by pointing out that with a name like that, he was obviously Russian.'

'Is he?'

'I heard that he's descended, via someone called Grand Duke Vasily Korsky-Rimsakov, from Catherine the Great herself.'

'Really?'

'I can't prove it. The Russians wouldn't want to let anything like that out. But I did find out that Boris' father, who insisted that the neighbours refer to him as "Your Highness", did in fact emigrate from Russia in 1918. He was a doorman at the Stork Club. The family lived in Hoboken.'

'He was quite a hero in Korea,' Dr. Waldowski said. 'His sergeant, a Cajun, got hit going up Heartbreak Ridge. Alexander — I knew Boris as PFC Alexander — threw him over his shoulder and carried him down through a hail of mortar fire. Both of them damned near died. I remember them both very clearly. As Boris worked his way through the nurses, the Sergeant — the Cajun — set up a still in the laboratory. Best White Lightning I ever had,' He paused thoughtfully. 'I've often wondered what happened to ol'

Horsey. Probably went back to his swamp and never left again.'

'*Horsey?*' Dr. Yancey inquired. 'Would that be Horsey de la Chevaux, by any chance?'

'Why, yes. Has Boris spoken of him?'

'Walter,' Dr. Yancey said. 'Hang onto your teeth. Have I got news for you!' He put his fingers in his mouth and whistled. Two boilermakers shortly thereafter came sliding with precision down the bar.

CHAPTER EIGHT

About five minutes before the convoy bearing His Islamic Highness, Crown Prince Hassan ad Kayam, Ambassador Extraordinary and Plenipotentiary to the French Republic, and his companions raced up to the front of the Paris Opera, two other fans of opera generally and of Boris Alexandrovich Korsky-Rimsakov in particular entered the building.

The two, a slight gentleman in his fifties and a tall, well-built gentleman in his middle thirties, entered the Opera through a door on the side of the building after emerging from the Place de l'Opera station of the Paris Metro (which is what they call the subway in Paris).

Both wore black suits, black shoes, black hats, and black shirts topped with reversed white collars, the customary civilian dress, so to speak, of clerics of the Roman Catholic persuasion. They were, in fact, vacationing clergymen.

They passed their tickets to one of the famous surly ticket-takers of the Paris Opera, were granted admission to the building, and made their way up several flights of narrow, poorly illuminated stairs to the third balcony, where they found seats that gave them a view of the stage and waited for the performance to begin.

The younger of the two, truth to tell, was having thoughts bordering on the irreverent. While he was much aware of the vows of chastity, obedience, and poverty he had taken when he had decided to become a priest, and regarded modesty as one of the nicer virtues, he thought this was a bit much.

He was the Very Reverend Monsignor Pancho de Malaga y de Villa, personal secretary to His Eminence the Archbishop of Swengchan, China. He was, in addition, very fond of the archbishop, whom he felt embodied all the characteristics of wisdom, piety, grace, modesty, and charm that all archbishops should but unfortunately do not always have.

He understood, in other words, the archbishop's reluctance to avail himself of the chauffeured limousine and cardinal's box that had been offered to them by the Cardinal-Archbishop of Paris. It was obviously far more in keeping with the vow of poverty they had taken to come to the opera by Metro instead of by limousine, and to sit in the third balcony instead of a box.

And he understood, he thought, His Eminence's motives in keeping the hand bearing the telltale bishop's ring jammed deep in his pocket, so that people would assume he was nothing more than a simple priest.

'Nice seats, Pancho, aren't they?' His Eminence said.

'With all respect, sir, I feel as if I'm looking at the stage through binoculars held backwards,' Monsignor de Malaga y de Villa replied.

'Boris' voice will fill the house, Pancho.'

'Might I suggest, Your Eminence, that if Maestro Korsky-Rimsakov knew that Your Eminence was in the house, it would give him great pleasure to see that we had better seats?'

'Yes, I'm sure it would,' the Archbishop of Swengchan replied. 'But I do so hate to disturb him before a performance.'

'He might be exercising, you mean?'

'Judge not, Pancho,' the archbishop replied, 'lest ye be judged. Despite what you might have heard, we don't know for certain, do we? In fact, these exercises we hear so much about might be nothing more than pushups and squat jumps.'

'Yes, I suppose so,' the monsignor agreed. He would have been more surprised to learn that the exercises were squat jumps and pushups than he would have been to hear that Boris had become a candidate for monastic orders, but, of course, he didn't say this.

Ten minutes later, the orchestra, which had been tuned up and ready to start for thirty minutes, began to play something that had nothing to do with the scheduled opera, *Benvenuto Cellini*. They began to play the trumpet fanfare from *Aïda*.

A hush fell over the house as some two thousand women sucked in their breath in anticipation. The trumpet fanfare from *Aïda* always indicated a rare personal appearance by *Cher Boris*. A spotlight flashed on the centre of the curtain. It was swept open and Boris Alexandrovich Korsky-Rimsakov stepped before the footlights.

The two thousand women in the audience who had sucked in their breath now let it out, together, in a moan of appreciation and awe. A wave of tumultuous applause, whistles, shrieks, and stamping feet shook the chandeliers.

Boris Alexandrovich Korsky-Rimsakov raised his hands above his head to acknowledge his reception and incidentally protect himself from the torrent of flowers, perfumed notes, hotel keys, and items of intimate feminine apparel that floated stageward from the audience, boxes, and balconies.

'Silence, my children!' Boris said, his voice, as the archbishop had said it would, quite filling the house. The house, save for the moans of a dozen or so women who had entered a semi-hysterical state at the sound of *Cher* Boris' voice, was immediately hushed.

'There are those among you,' Maestro Korsky-Rimsakov said, 'who will leave here tonight convinced that tonight I have sung even more superbly than I do normally. And you will be right. Tonight I am deeply motivated.'

He paused, grandly acknowledging the cheers and applause.

'Most of you, I know, are aware of my distinguished military record,' Boris went on, 'And of what the president of the United States, in my Distinguished Service Cross citation, referred to as "the grievous wounds" I suffered while carrying a wounded comrade through a murderous hail of small arms, machine gun, mortar, and artillery fire.'*

---

*This is, oddly enough, perfectly true. The fact that PFC Alexander was motivated by that fact Sergeant Chevaux alone knew the location of the platoon's cache of White Lightning and that his loss on the field of battle would have meant the loss of the White Lightning may be germane, but it cannot detract from the fact that PFC Alexander did in fact carry his platoon sergeant four miles through the hail of fire, suffering eleven wounds while doing so.

There was applause and cheering, and the trumpet section of the opera's orchestra played eight bars of 'The Stars and Stripes Forever' before *Cher* Boris hushed them with a wave of his hand.

'I was, of course, hospitalised after my ordeal. The world very nearly lost the greatest voice since Caruso. But I was saved, ladies and gentlemen, by the finest collection of practitioners of the Hippocratic art since the Greek himself, banded together in what the army, for reasons I don't pretend to comprehend, called the 4077th MASH. It possibly may have had something to do with the fact that the chief surgeon, the beloved Dr. Hawkeye Pierce, operated a rather splendid still in his tent, but that's neither here nor there.

'What *is* important, my friends, is that one of that collection of noble healers, one of that band of sainted Samaritans, one of those medical geniuses who saved me for you and the rest of the world, is here tonight in the Paris Opera.

'Ladies and gentlemen, I sing tonight for Dr. Walter Waldowski and for his charming wife and daughter.' He gestured toward the Diamond Circle of boxes, then bowed low and with becoming modesty. Still bent over, he raised his eyes and saw that something had gone awry.

'Turn the spotlight on, you bumbling idiot!' he shouted. The light finally came on, swept across the Diamond Circle, and came to rest on the Presidential (formerly the Imperial) Box.

'I see that Dr. Waldowski is not there,' Boris said. 'He has obviously been called away to come to the aid of someone in need. Greater love hath no man than to give up one of my performances to help his fellow man. Stand up, Mrs. Waldowski, and take a bow!'

'Oh, my,' the Archbishop of Swengchan said to Monsignor de Malaga y de Villa. 'Isn't that a pleasant coincidence! I've thought of Dr. Waldowski so often over the years.'

'I'll bet,' the monsignor replied.

'Captain Waldowski was one of ours, Pancho,' the archbishop said.* 'As a matter of fact, he was the only one who was. We had Baptists and Episcopalians, Lutherans, Methodists, Jews, and even an Existential Buddhist. But only two Catholics – Dr. Waldowski and me.'

'You left out our sister in the God Is Love in All Forms Christian Church, Your Eminence,' the monsignor said.

'Oh, that was long before Hot Lips ... excuse me – Reverend Mother Wilson – found religion,' the archbishop said. 'In those days, she was just a nurse. A very good nurse, but just a nurse. I don't think she even went to church much in those days.'

Monsignor de Malaga y de Villa waited until the house lights dimmed and the curtain opened on act one of *Benvenuto Cellini*. Then he excused himself.

'I'll be right back, Your Eminence,' he said.

'You should have thought of that before the opera started, Pancho,' the archbishop said. 'Now you'll miss Boris' singing.'

The monsignor did not reply.

He went down three flights of stairs to the door marked DIAMOND CIRCLE – ADMISSION BY TICKET ONLY· He was going to the Presidential box to tell this old friend of the archbishop's that the archbishop was here. He knew it would make his superior and his friend happy, and he knew that unless he went after the man himself, the archbishop would do nothing – he wouldn't want to intrude.

The monsignor made it two steps inside the door before he was suddenly brought to a halt by a ham-sized hand extended in front of his face.

'You have a ticket, Father?' the usher demanded suspiciously.

---

*At an early stage in his ecclesiastical career, the Archbishop of Swengchan, His Eminence John Patrick Mulcahy, served as Captain, Chaplain's Corps, U.S. Army Reserve. He was attached for eighteen months to the 4077th MASH, Eighth United States Army, then located near Chorwon, Korea.

'I wish to go to the Presidential Box,' the monsignor replied.

'Everybody wishes to go to the Presidential box,' the usher replied. 'The question I asked you, Father, was whether or not you have a ticket permitting you to be in the Diamond Circle?'

'I'm afraid not,' the monsignor said. 'But —'

'Shame on you!' the usher said. 'A man of the cloth trying to sneak in where he's not allowed. That's really disgraceful behaviour for a priest. You *are* a priest, aren't you?'

'Actually,' Pancho said, 'I'm a monsignor,'

'That's even worse!' the usher said.

'Listen, this is important. I have to see the doctor in the Presidential Box.'

'That's a likely story?'

'I'm a monsignor. Would I lie?'

'That depends on whether or not you're really a monsignor,' the usher said with calm logic. 'And if you really are a monsignor, whether or not you work at it.'

'I tell you I'm a monsignor!'

'Did I hear the title "monsignor"?' an American voice inquired. The monsignor looked up and saw a bishop in ecclesiastical garb — a black smock-like affair around the ample waist of which was a bishop's purple sash — sweeping up to him. 'It's probably someone looking for me.'

'Your Excellency,' the usher said politely, 'this *person*, who says he is a monsignor, is trying to sneak into the Diamond Circle.'

'Are you a monsignor?' the bishop asked.

'Monsignor Pancho de Malaga y de Villa at your service,' Pancho said.

'And are you looking for me?'

'Forgive me, I don't know who you are,' Pancho said.

'I am the Bishop of Greater Miami and the florida Keys,' the man said.

'Your Excellency,' Pancho said, 'I have the honour to be personal secretary to His Eminence John Patrick Mulcahy, Archbishop of Swengchan.'

'That's a funny name for a Chinese archbishop,' the bishop mused. 'But no matter. How may I be of service to the archbishop?'

'Your Excellency,' Pancho said, 'I wish to tell a doctor now in the Presidential box that His Eminence, an old friend, is in the house.'

'You look a little young to be a monsignor,' the bishop said. 'But things aren't the way they used to be in the Church. And if you were an imposter, why would you say you're only a lowly monsignor? If you're a fake, it would be just as easy to say you're a bishop.'

'I don't wish to stay in the Diamond Circle, Your Excellency,' Pancho said. 'I just wish to deliver the message and then leave.'

'Nonsense,' the Bishop of Greater Miami and the Florida Keys said. 'His Eminence the Cardinal-Archbishop of Paris has let me use his box. I offer it to your archbishop. I mean, after all, if we don't scratch each other's backs, where are we?'

'That's one way of putting it, Your Excellency,' Pancho replied.

'I place myself at the service of your archbishop,' the bishop said. 'We will go to the Presidential box.'

'I hope you know what you're doing, Bishop,' the usher said. 'This guy don't look like a monsignor to me.'

'Trust me,' the bishop said. 'Show me the way to the Presidential Box.'

With the bishop and Pancho marching along behind him, the usher led the way to the Presidential Box. The usher threw the curtain back and bowed them in.

There were three people in the box – two females, sitting in a sort of trance staring glassy-eyed at the stage (where *Cher* Boris was singing), and a short, plump, Arabian gentleman snoring gently in his chair, his mouth agape.

The bishop coughed, and then coughed again much louder. Mrs. Waldowski finally turned around. In Hamtramck, when her parish priest managed to get her name right, she basked in the sense of clerical approval for weeks. But this wasn't Hamtramck.

'Sssshhh!' she hissed ferociously. 'Can't you hear? *Cher* Boris is singing!'

Monsignor de Malaga y de Villa walked to the short, plump, Arabian gentleman and shook him. His Royal Highness Crown Prince Hassan ad Kayam closed his mouth and opened his eyes.

'Hey, Pancho!' he said. 'How are you?'

'Sssshhh!' Mrs. Wilma Waldowski said.

'Sssshhh! Ssshhh! For heaven's sake!' Miss Wanda Waldowski hissed.

'Where's Dr. Waldowski?' Pancho whispered.

'Probably in Harry's New York Bar with T. Mullins Yancey,' His Highness whispered back. 'They were both a little plastered the last time I saw them. You here by yourself, or with Dago Red?'

Monsignor de Malaga y de Villa, perhaps understandably – Mrs. and Miss Waldowski were hissing at him like a pair of infuriated pythons – forgot himself.

'With Dago Red,' he said.

'Who, might I inquire,' the bishop somewhat haughtily inquired, 'is "Dago Red"?'

'Forgive me, Your Excellency,' Pancho said. 'Sometimes ... I don't approve, of course, and I am ashamed, but sometimes they call His Eminence that.'

'You stand there, with your face hanging out, and try to tell me that *anyone* would dare call an archbishop, a high-ranking prelate of the Church, "Dago Red"?'

'I'm afraid so, Your Excellency,' Pancho admitted.

'You, sir,' the Bishop of Greater Miami and the Florida Keys said, drawing himself up to his full five feet six and one half inches and placing his hands on his purple sash, 'couldn't *possibly* be a monsignor. Monsignori do *not* refer to archbishops as "Dago Red." You, you scalawag, have conned a bishop! God will get you for that!'

And with that, he turned and marched out of the box.

91

The usher looked at the bishop.

'Is it or isn't it?' he asked.

'Is it or isn't it *what*?' His Highness replied.

'Sssssssshhhhhh!' Mrs. Waldowski said.

'Is it a monsignor or isn't it?'

'It doesn't matter,' Pancho said, emerging from the Presidential Box, 'I'm leaving.' He was a little sick at heart. It would have been a good thing for His Eminence to get together with an old friend, for His Eminence was in Paris on a vacation ordered by the Highest Authority. But this Waldowski was obviously no better than the others with whom His Eminence had served in the army. The monsignor had met many of them, and, to a man (and, in the case of former Major Margaret 'Hot-Lips' Houlihan, woman), they exhibited what the monsignor regarded as an excessive fondness for the grape. The one thing the archbishop didn't need on his vacation was association with a bunch of booze hounds.

He went back up the three flights of narrow, badly-lighted stairs and resumed his seat beside the archbishop.

'I was afraid you had become lost, Pancho,' the archbishop said.

'Not quite, Your Eminence,' the monsignor replied.

When the final curtain fell on *Benvenuto Cellini* it took His Eminence and the monsignor far longer to get out of the Opera than it had taken them to get in, because those the management thought of as the riffraff in the upper balconies were not permitted to leave until all those in the orchestra and the two lower tiers of balconies had marched down the main staircase and been ushered into their limousines.

It came to pass, then, as it says in the Good Book, that, by coincidence, the archbishop and the monsignor left the side door of the Opera only moments before the convoy bearing the star of the performance was ready to drive away from said star's private entrance.

Crown Prince Hassan's limousine contained Boris, Mrs.

and Miss Waldowski, and the crown prince. A hastily summoned Hertz limousine, in line behind the prince's car, now carried the Baroness d'Iberville and Esmeralda Hoffenburg, the ballerina, who were members of the entourage.

(Sometimes the maestro liked to exercise after a performance as well as before it, not to mention during the intermission, and ladies had learned to hold themselves in readiness for the privilege of contributing to the world of art. There had been some initial confusion at first when the baroness had understandably come to think that Mrs. and Miss Waldowski had, so to speak, moved in on the maestro, but His Royal Highness had explained the situation to her and smoothed the matter over.)

Mrs. Waldowski, who was still somewhat dazed, accepted without question the maestro's announcement that Dr. Waldowski had gone with Dr. Yancey at his specific request to Harry's New York Bar to make sure the beer was at the proper temperature.

'With my delicate pipes, dear lady,' Boris said, 'one cannot be too careful.'

'I understand, Maestro. I may call you Maestro, mayn't I?'

'The customary form of address is "*Dear* Maestro," ' Boris replied, 'but what the hell, you're the Painless Pole's wife, so I'll make an exception in your case.'

'I had no idea you knew my husband, Dear Maestro,' she said.

'One of the great men of the world,' Boris replied. Then the world's greatest opera singer glanced out the limousine window and proceeded to let a yell escape from his magnificent throat. 'I'll be god-damned!'

'I beg your pardon?'

'It couldn't be,' Boris said. 'If he were in Paris, he would have called me. He knows how much I love him. But, on the other hand, I'm never wrong.' He picked up the microphone and spoke to the chauffeur.

'Turn around!' he ordered.

'Turn around? *Cher* Maestro, that's impossible!' the chauffeur protested.

It was a reasonable protest. The limousine, preceded and trailed by motorcycle policemen, was moving slowly through hordes of people – those who had left the opera after witnessing the performance as well as those not fortunate enough to have been able to get tickets who had nevertheless come to the Place de l'Opera in hopes of seeing *Cher* Boris, and, frankly, to gawk at the hoi-polloi.

Making a U turn would have been quite impossible. Boris sat forward on the finely tooled Moroccan leather seat, peered out the window, and saw this for himself.

'Stop the car!' he ordered. The limousine slid to a halt. Boris leaned further forward, flipped a conveniently located switch on the partition that separated them from the chauffeur, and waited impatiently while a purring electric motor slid a panel in the roof open. The moment there was room for his massive shoulders to pass through the opening, he stood up on the seat and rose through the roof.

'I knew it was him!' he said. 'I have the eyes of an eagle.'

He popped back into the car.

'Hassan,' he ordered, 'have someone go to Harry's New York Bar to pick up the doctors. Have them carried to Maxim's. It's reunion time!'

As Hassan reached for the car telephone, Boris came back through the roof. He took in a deep breath, put his fingers between his teeth, and emitted a piercing whistle that could be heard from the Tuileries Gardens to the American Express Building.

The huge crowd, somewhat stunned, was immediately hushed. Ten thousand pairs of eyes turned to the singer.

He stood with his fist clenched, his arm over his head, making pumping motions. As any ex-U.S. Army infantryman well knows, this is the standard signal for 'Form on me.' As there were only a few ex-U.S. Army infantrymen in the throng, however, most people formed the impression

94

that *Cher* Boris was making threatening gestures at the Opera House, and naturally wondered what the Opera had done to pique *Cher* Boris.

'Dago Red!' Boris bellowed. 'Dago Red! Over here, Dago Red!'

CHAPTER NINE

Far back in the crowd, the Very Reverend Pancho de Malaga y de Villa turned to the Archbishop of Swengchan.

'I believe Mr. Korsky-Rimsakov is trying to attract your attention, Your Eminence.'

The archbihop, a little smile on his face, raised his clenched fist above his head and moved it up and down in a pumping motion. As every former chaplain who has seen combat with the United States Army well knows, this is the officially prescribed signal for 'Your signal understood, am forming on you.'

The Bishop of Greater Miami and the Florida Keys, however, had not been privileged to serve as a chaplain in ground combat. Thus deprived of the information upon which to base a proper analysis of what was going on, he based his analysis on what he saw. The opera singer, for reasons he couldn't imagine, was shaking his fist at a clergyman, and the clergyman, by shaking *his* fist, was accepting the challenge to battle.

'Make way for Dago Red!' Boris bellowed, gesturing with his hands. 'Make way for Dago Red!' The crowd parted like the Red Sea in Cecil B. DeMille's rather well-known Biblical epic.

The Bishop of Greater Miami and the Florida Keys, after a moment's hesitation (this sort of thing was, after all, the function of younger priests fresh from the seminary, not of a bishop – particularly one who had, since he was to ride in the Cardinal-Archbishop's car and use his box, seen fit to attend the opera in ecclesiastical uniform), rushed forward to do his duty as he saw that duty.

He would, he decided, since he was unmistakably a bishop, *order* the priest who was willing to engage in fisticuffs on the street in front of Van Cleef & Arpels to cease and desist. Obedience, he reminded himself, was one of the vows taken by all priests.

But the moment he pushed his way through the crowd and found himself standing in the passage Boris had ordered formed, his hand raised, like a traffic policeman's, in the gesture to stop, he saw that *two* men were coming down the passageway through the crowd. The second one he recognised. It was the man he had encountered in the Diamond Circle, the one who had made the preposterous (not to say irreverent and possibly blasphemous) allegation that he was a monsignor.

There came another piercing whistle, so loud that the Bishop of Greater Miami and the Florida Keys involuntarily hunched his shoulders against the sound. It was, after a very brief pause, repeated. Almost involuntarily, the bishop turned to look at the source of the awful noise. When he turned, he saw that the bearded man sticking out of the roof of the Cadillac limousine was pointing at him. He looked not unlike Uncle Sam in the recruiting posters.

'I knew you weren't to be trusted when I heard you sing,' Boris called to him in a voice nearly as piercing as his whistle. 'And now I catch you compounding the sin of being drunk on stage and singing off-key with the sin of making off with the bishop's costume.' He paused, located a sergeant of the Gendarmerie Nationale, and called to him.

'Sergeant,' he ordered, 'throw that fat, off-key scoundrel in the Bastille. After, of course, making sure he returns his costume to wardrobe.'

Almost instantly, the crowd began to make menacing noises, the Bishop of Greater Miami and the Florida Keys felt strong hands on his arms. He was lifted off his feet, and, carried between two enormous gendarmes, rushed toward the Paris equivalent of a paddy wagon. The last thing he heard before the doors slammed shut on him was the bearded man's final shout:

'Dago Red, you and Pancho get in the car with the broads. We're all filled up in here.'

97

The Archbishop of Swengchan opened the door to the second limousine.

'Why,' he said, 'if it isn't the Baroness d'Iberville and Miss Hoffenburg!* What a pleasant surprise. You remember Monsignor de Malaga y de Villa, of course, ladies?'

The smile on the monsignor's face appeared a bit strained. He sat, looking a bit uncomfortable, on the jump seat; the archbishop sat between the ladies.

Esmeralda Hoffenburg, the ballerina, looked at the monsignor.

'Quelle pitie,' she said. 'Quel perdu!'†

'Will you have a little bubbly, Your Eminence?' the Baroness d'Iberville asked, handing him a champagne glass.

'Why, that's very kind of you, Baroness,' the archbishop said. 'And why not? This is a very happy occasion for me.'

In the limousine immediately in front of the Hoffenburg-d'Iberville vehicle, Boris Alexandrovich Korsky-Rimsakov, having seen his friends safely inside the trailing limousine, slipped back into his seat.

'What are you waiting for?' he demanded. 'Take us to Maxim's. As I said before, it's reunion time!'

Mrs. Waldowski, who had of course heard of Maxim's Restaurant, had had it on her list of PLACES TO EAT IN PARIS. She had heard, of course, that it was one of the world's most famous, and certainly most elegant (and therefore expensive),

---

*His Eminence had previously met the ladies in an official capacity. He had married J. Robespierre O'Reilly and Madame Christina Korsky-Rimsakov, the singer's sister, in ceremonies in Las Vegas, Nevada. Accounts of the affair may be found both in the *Innkeeper's Journal* ('Biggest Vegas Wedding Blast Ever Is Boffo for Nero's Villa Cash Box') and, in a more scholarly treatment of what transpired, in *M*A*S*H Goes to Las Vegas.*

†For that one half of one percent of the readers of this volume who are not absolutely fluent in French: 'What a pity. What a loss.' Monsignor de Malaga y de Villa had been, before taking Holy Orders, both a champion skier and a five-goal polo player. He stood six-foot-two and weighed one hundred ninety-five pounds.

restaurants. 'But what the hell,' she had thought in her heart of hearts, 'you only live once, so why not?'

Her first attempt to eat at Maxim's had met with failure. She had been stopped two feet inside the door by a cold-eyed Frenchman in a dinner jacket. The dinner jacket, to be sure, had seen better days, and in her housewifely professional opinion, the boiled shirt sorely needed the attention of a Magic Detergent, but the wearer of same didn't let this faze him.

'Without reservations, madame,' he icily informed her, 'seating you is absolutely out of zee question.'

Undaunted, she had returned to her hotel, telephoned for reservations, and been informed that they were booked solidly through 1982. One of Dr. Waldowski's little philosophical observations ('Money talks') had then come to her mind, and she had a little chat with the concierge at the Ritz. At first he too had made it plain that she couldn't hope to get inside, but as she had continued to stuff his breast pocket with the odd-looking pieces of paper the French used for money; he had changed his mind.

'No promises, mind you,' he had said, straightening out the paper money before stuffing it in his sock, 'but as a special favour, I will see what I can do.'

Reservations had finally been obtained for four-thirty in the afternoon. Mrs. Waldowski and Wanda had been led through four outer dining-rooms and up a dark stairway and installed in a *chamber separée* not a foot wider than a phone booth. After a long delay, a haughty waiter (who had made it quite plain to both of them that he was serving them only as a penance for some unspeakable sin) presented them with a slice of liverwurst, a badly singed pork chop, some cold and lumpy potatoes, and a decanter of red wine so sour Mrs. Waldowski had made the terrible gaffe of believing it was vinegar and had poured it over the one-eighth of a tomato and two limp pieces of lettuce served as the salad.

The bill for *pâté de la maison, cotelette de porc Louis XIV*,

99

pommes des terres Bourbonnaise, salade Richelieu, and *Burgundy Haute Criomble '52* had come to $106.50 on the bill presented by the waiter, who had hovered over their table while they were eating doing everything but lifting their elbows for them in order to get them out of the place as quickly as possible.

Mrs. Waldowski was, then, more than a little surprised when the limousine rolled up before Maxim's and she saw a dozen waiters lined up in two ranks by the door and the maître d'hôtel himself bowing as he opened the limousine door.

Boris Alexandrovich Korsky-Rimsakov exited the limousine first. The sommelier, with the badge of his office (the key to the wine cellar) hanging around his neck, emerged from the restaurant at a half trot, bearing a single glass on a silver tray.

'Maxim's is honoured,' the mâitre d'hôtel said to the singer.

'We all make mistakes, I'm told,' Boris replied. 'I have decided to give you another chance – out of the goodness of my heart, and against my better judgment.'

'Our *Cher* Boris is as kind and gracious as he is a great singer.'

'I know,' Boris replied. He picked the martini glass off the tray and took a generous sip. He rolled it around in his mouth, looked thoughtful, and then spit it out.

'Too warm by at least eight degrees,' he said. 'And far, far too much vermouth. But an improvement over your last attempt.'

'Oh, thank you, *Cher* Maestro,' the maître d'hôtel said, 'there will, of course, be no bill tonight.'

'Was there ever any question that there would be?' Boris asked. 'If I were to pay for my supper, I would certainly go somewhere where they at least know how to make a simple martini.'

'If you will be so good as to follow me, Maestro,' the maître d'hôtel said.

'You have no foul little plot in mind to put me on display

100

so that my presence here will lend a little class to your joint, do you?'

'I thought perhaps the maestro would be happy in the Imperial Hall.'

'Get rid of the fiddle players and put up screens so that my friends and I won't be gawked at, and it will suffice,' Boris said.

'Your wish, Maestro, is our command,' the maître d'hôtel said, as he bowed Boris into the restaurant between the rows of bowing waiters.

'Yes, I know. Have some phones brought in,' Boris said. 'I have some calls to make.'

A table in the shape of a U had been set up in the Imperial Hall. The crystal and silver gleamed in the light from the chandelier. At the centre of the U a large chair had been set up, and, as the party moved inside, two wine stewards and two waiters rushed forward with champagne bottles and glasses, oysters on the half shell, and cold salmon.

'Something to whet your appetite, *Cher* Maestro,' the maître d'hôtel said. 'I hope you won't think I'm presumptuous.'

'I won't unless you're trying to slip us some of your lousy Frog oysters,' *Cher* Boris said.

'These were flown in this morning from Maine, *Cher* Maestro.'

Boris turned and spoke with Mrs. Waldowski. 'These are safe to eat, Madame Waldowski,' he said. 'Presuming he's not prevaricating again. They come from the Finest Kind Fish Market and Medical Clinic.'

'Oh, really?' Mrs. Waldowski said.

'Hassan, get Hawkeye on the phone,' Boris said to His Royal Highness. He turned to Mrs. Waldowski. 'Sit down. Madame, and have a little bubbly,' he said, 'while we await your distinguished husband, the great tooth mechanic.'

'Oh, *Cher* Maestro?' Mrs. Waldowski said, as a waiter held a chair for her with the utmost deference. 'I'm simply overwhelmed.'

'That's the general idea,' Boris replied. 'Nothing is too good for the good lady of the Painless Polack.' He looked back at Hassan, snatched the telephone from his hands, and spoke. 'Hawkeye! Boris, here.' There was a pause. 'What do you mean, you're the Paris overseas operator? We've been trying for hours to place this call and we're no further than the local operator? Are you aware that this is your *Cher* Maestro speaking?' Another pause. Boris took a deep breath. 'Cee-les-tial Ai—eeeee-da!' he sang at full volume. Another pause, this one with an aside to those at the table: 'I guess that'll prove it.' Then again speaking to the telephone: 'Might I have the great privilege of speaking with Dr. Benjamin Franklin Pierce? This is Boris Alexandrovich Korsky-Rimsakov speaking.' Charm oozed from every syllable.

He covered the phone with his hand. 'Have to treat his old lady with kid gloves. She's got a temper you wouldn't believe,' he said to the others. He uncovered the phone. 'What do you mean, he's *clamming*? You mean he's out there on the Spruce Harbour mud flats again, grubbing around on his hands and knees?' Another aside to those at the table; this time he forgot to cover the phone with his hand: 'A brilliant surgeon, certainly. But more than a little strange. Odd. Weird.' His face assumed a pained look.

'Dear lady, whatever gave you the impression I was talking about your husband?'

Shrill sounds suggesting outrage came from the receiver, filling the room. Boris held the telephone six inches from his ear. His eye fell on Mrs. Waldowski. He thrust the telephone at her. 'Here, my dear, you speak with her,' he said. 'You have a good deal in common. See if you can't get her to summon her husband to the telephone.'

That problem out of the way, he turned back to Hassan and again snatched away the phone the prince had to his ear.

'This is Boris Alexandrovich Korsky-Rimsakov speaking. With whom am I speaking?' Pause. 'Ah, yes,' he said. 'Brother, using the term loosely, de Wilde. Where is the Reverend Mother?' Pause. 'Hot Lips, this is Boris,' he said.

'you'll never guess who I'm having dinner with this very moment.' Pause. 'How could I ever forget that you're the Reverend Mother Emeritus? It's nothing like that.' He looked over the table, stood up, and handed the telephone to His Eminence John Patrick Mulcahy, Archbishop of Swengchan.

'Talk to her, Dago Red,' Boris said. 'For reasons I can't imagine, Hot Lips thinks I'm drunk and calling from a borde – not from here.'

The archbishop took the telephone. 'Margaret? Father Mulcahy. How are you, my dear?'

Monsignor de Malaga y de Villa looked pained.

Boris, smiling a smile of contentment, searched the sea of faces at and surrounding the table, found that of the maître d'hôtel, gestured to him, and ordered, 'Bring on the booze! What are you waiting for?'

The world's greatest opera singer, both in fact and according to the legend that had been embroidered in golden thread on the back of his silk pyjamas by an adoring fan, lay groaning piteously on silken sheets, his head buried beneath a silken pillow.

He finally pushed the pillow off his head, opened one eye, and peered out the window.

'Oh my God!' he said in absolute shock and horror.

'Somehow, I don't think that was said in prayer,' the Archbishop of Swengchan said. Boris rolled over and looked at him. The archbishop was sitting up in the second of the two beds in the room, wearing a cotton nightshirt and drinking a cup of tea.

'Thank God you're here, Dago Red,' Boris said. 'You know me. You can tell Him I always meant well. He'll believe you. You must have some influence.'

The archbishop said nothing for a moment. 'Would you like some tea, Boris?' he asked.

'That proves it,' he said. 'Hell isn't hellfire and brimstone. It's ice and snow from horizon to horizon and your best friend offering someone in my condition a cup of tea.'

'As ye sow, Boris, so shall ye reap!' the archbishop said.

'Tea and piety and ice and snow,' Boris said. 'I'd rather have the hellfire and brimstone.'

'How about some coffee?'

'You mean, I have a choice?'

The door opened, and His Royal Highness Prince Hassan, also in night clothes, stepped in.

'Are you awake, *Cher* Boris?' he asked.

'Thank God you're here, Hassan. I wouldn't want to be down here all alone. Furthermore, most of my troubles can be blamed on evil companions. You, in particular. I'll tell Him that.'

'What's he talking about, Dago Red?' Hassan asked.

'I don't know,' the archbishop replied. 'But then, I seldom do know what he's talking about.'

'You mean, Hassan, that you *don't* know? That you haven't looked out the window?'

Hassan obligingly looked out the window.

'What am I supposed to see?'

'I see miles and miles of nothing but snow and ice. What do you see?'

'The same thing,' Hassan said.

'And that doesn't *bother* you? The prospect of going through eternity with cold toes and the sniffles?'

'It won't be quite that long, Boris,' Hassan said. 'I came in to tell you that we just heard on the radio that Horsey and François Mulligan will land in about five minutes.'

'I'm dreaming, that's what it is,' Boris said suddenly, and with certainty in his voice. He reached up and pinched his cheek. He yelped in pain.

'I'm almost afraid to ask what that was all about,' the archbishop said. 'But my curiosity's got the best of me. Why did you pinch your cheek so hard that it hurt, Boris?'

'To wake up from this entirely unpleasant nightmare,' Boris replied reasonably. 'No offence, Dago Red.'

'None taken,' the archbishop said.

'This is somewhat confusing,' Boris said finally, sitting up and putting his hands to his head with infinite tenderness. 'If I pinched myself so hard that it hurt in order to wake up, how come I'm still here, barely able to bear the pain of my exquisite agony? And why is all that ice and snow still out there, horizon to horizon?' He peered out the window again.

'Here comes a helicopter,' he said. 'A red one. I would have thought that He would travel around in something that had a little more class. Maybe in a golden chariot; maybe on a white cloud.'

'That's probably Horsey and François,' Hassan said. 'I told you they radioed that they were almost here.'

'Not that *I* don't know, of course, where we are,' Boris said. 'But I want to make sure *you* know where we are. Where *are* we, Hassan?'

'On the North Slope of Alaska, Boris, near Prudhoe Bay.'

'Of course, of course,' Boris said. 'That explains all that goddamn ice and snow. And the next question, obviously, is — what the *hell* are we doing in Alaska?'

'Boris,' the archbishop said. 'If I asked you, would you reply truthfully?'

'Asked me what?'

'Where you *thought* you were?'

'You wouldn't do that to me, old buddy, would you?'

'I might,' the archbishop said. 'But perhaps not just now.'

'I suppose you know, Dago Red, what we're doing here? It sounds like something you'd think up.'

'It was your idea, Boris,' Hassan said, a tone of surprise in his voice. 'It came to you while you and the Painless Polack and T. Mullins Yancey were flying paper airplanes off the Eiffel Tower.'

'Yes, of course it did,' Boris replied. 'You didn't think I'd forgotten, did you?' He paused. 'But do *you* remember why I wanted to come to Alaska?'

'You decided we all had to go to Miami, Boris,' the archbishop said.

'My God! How much whisky did you force me to drink,

Hassan? Miami is even worse than the North Slope of Alaska. You must have misunderstood me.'

'You *do* remember talking to Margaret on the overseas telephone, don't you, Boris?' the archbishop asked.

'Margaret? Margaret who? I don't know anyone amed Margaret. . . . Oh, you mean Hot Lips. Yes, of course, I remember talking to her.'

'The important thing, Boris,' Archbishop Mulcahy went on, 'is whether you remember *what* you talked about.'

'It's a good thing for you, Dago Red, that I have a profound admiration for those who serve the Church. Otherwise, I wouldn't take kindly to the suggestion that I was drunk out of my mind and don't remember what I said.'

'I'm glad you remember,' Mulcahy said. 'I would hate to think that you'd forgotten.'

'Perish the thought,' Boris said. 'You say we're going to Miami?'

'Just as soon as we get Horsey and François on board the plane.'

'Wake me when we get there,' Boris said, lying back on the bed and pulling the silk pillow over his head again. 'I sang last night, you know, and I need my rest.'

CHAPTER TEN

FROM INTERPOL PARIS
TO F.B.I. WASHINGTON D.C.

CENTRAL PARIS REGION GENDARMERIE NATIONALE ARE
HOLDING A SUSPECT CHARGED WITH GRAND THEFT OF
COSTUMES BELONG TO THE PARIS NATIONAL OPERA AND
RESISTING ARREST. SUSPECT WAS APPREHENDED IN THE
VICINITY OF THE OPERA WHILE ATTIRED IN VESTMENTS OF
A BISHOP OF CATHOLIC CHURCH. SUSPECT HAD NO
IDENTITY PAPERS. SUSPECT FIRMLY MAINTAINS HE IS
PATRICK MICHAEL O'GROGARTY, AMERICAN NATIONAL,
EMPLOYED AS BISHOP OF DIOCESE OF GREATER MIAMI
AND THE FLORIDA KEYS. SUBJECT IS MALE CAUCASIAN,
APPROXIMATELY FIFTY-FIVE YEARS OLD, HAZEL EYES,
GREY HAIR, FIVE FEET SIX INCHES TALL AND WEIGHING
190 POUNDS, FLUSHED COMPLEXION AND STOCKY BUILD.
GENDARMERIE NATIONALE AUTHORITIES BELIEVE HE IS
IRISH, BUT DOUBT, BECAUSE OF LANGUAGE SUSPECT HAS
BEEN USING, THAT HE IS CONNECTED WITH ANY RELIGIOUS
BODY. GENDARMERIE NATIONALE FEELS IT IS MOST
PROBABLE HE IS MEMBER OF IRISH REPUBLICAN ARMY,
AND INQUIRY IS BEING MADE OF BRITISH AND REPUBLIC
OF IRELAND AUTHORITIES. PLEASE ADVISE.

J. MORGENBLAU, INSPECTOR IN CHARGE
INTERPOL PARIS

'Chancellory of the Diocese of Greater Miami and the
Florida Keys. Good morning.'

'Good morning. I wonder, if he's not tied up or anything,
if I might speak with the bishop?'

'Might I inquire who's calling?'

'I'd rather not say, if it's all the same to you. I won't take but a moment of his time.'

'Well, I'm sorry, sir, we just can't let just *anyone* speak with the bishop.'

'This is a very personal matter.'

'I'm sorry, sir, we have our rules. You just can't run a diocese without rules, as I'm sure you'll agree.'

'Very well. This is the F.B.I.'

'The F.B.I.! As in Federal Bureau of Investigation?'

'Correct. Now put me through to the bishop.'

'I'm afraid I can't do that, sir.'

'What do you mean, you can't do that? This is the F.B.I. calling!'

'So you say. But how do I know that?'

'Because I'm *telling* you, that's why!'

'But certainly, sir, you must realize that just anyone at all could call up and say he's from the F.B.I. How do I know you're not an impostor?'

'I want your name and social security number,' the man from the F.B.I. said officiously.

'I'm sorry, sir, we are not permitted to give out that information.'

'Why not? All we want is the facts.'

'Right on the bottom of my social security card it says, in big letters, "Not to be used for purposes of identification." Are you asking me to defy the Social Security Administration? Shame on you! So far as I'm concerned that proves you're an impostor, up to God only knows what nefarious scheme. Good day, sir.'

The phone went dead in the ear of the agent in charge, Miami area Federal Bureau of Investigation. But he hadn't become an agent in charge by giving up easily.

'Finklestein,' he said to his deputy agent in charge, 'there's something fishy going on over there. I can feel it in my bones. Who's our undercover informant in the chancellory?'

'I hate to tell you this, Chief,' deputy agent in charge

Finklestein confessed, 'but we don't have one at the moment. We're working on it, and the situation should be corrected within the foreseeable future, but at the moment, we just don't have an informant.'

'Just two months ago — no more, I remember — I O.K.'d the expenditure of some of our secret funds to pay for an informer at the chancellory.'

'I hate to tell you this, Chief,' deputy-agent-in-charge Finklestein said. 'I'd hoped to break it to you gently when the time was right and we had corrected the situation.'

'Stop beating around the bush!' the agent in charge said. 'You can't ever expect to become an agent in charge yourself if you can't answer a simple question.'

'He defected, Chief,' deputy agent-in-charge Finklestein said.

'*Defected?*' the agent in charge said, incredulously.

'Defected,' Finklestein repeated firmly. 'They got to him, Chief. One of our best men, too.'

'Just give me the facts, Finklestein.'

'A week ago come Thursday, he became a monk,' Finklestein said.

'That's awful! He'll tell them everything he knows.'

'It's not as bad as it first appeared to be, Chief. He talked to me before he made the move.'

'You knew it was going to happen? And you didn't stop him? Why didn't you have him locked up?'

'He outwitted me, Chief,' Finklestein said. 'I told you, before he turned traitor, he was one of our best men. He planned his defection very carefully.'

'You should have had him thrown in the slammer for cheating on his income tax,' the agent in charge said firmly.

'How could I know if he had?'

'Everybody does, stupid!' the agent in charge replied. 'And when we can't catch somebody fair and square, we always have that. You just weren't *thinking*, Finklestein. You let the side down.'

'You didn't let me finish, Chief,' Finklestein said. 'I told you, he came to me and told me he was, as he put it, going to change sides.'

'He came and told you that, and you let him go! We've been over that before.'

'But he told me he wasn't going to blow the whistle on us,' Finklestein said.

'Ha!' the agent in charge snorted. 'At this very moment he's singing his head off, the lousy canary!'

'Not so, Chief,' Finklestein said. 'He didn't become an ordinary, or talking, monk. He joined the other kind.'

'*What* other kind?'

'The kind in Kentucky that don't talk. Trappists, I think.'

'Sounds subversive to me,' the agent in charge said. 'They don't talk at *all*?'

'Not a word.'

'You're sure?'

'Positive. And our man, our ex-man, promised me, Boy Scout's honour, that he'd stay there for at least a year, until we had time, as he put it, to "cover our tracks." '

'Well, that was certainly decent of him — for a rotten defector monk, I mean.'

'I thought so, Chief,' Finklestein agreed.

'But the bottom line, when you get to it, Fink, is that we don't have anybody in the chancellory *now*, do we?'

'Afraid not, Chief. We're working on it, but the best we've been able to do is send a gilder over.'

'What's a gilder?'

'You know that gold cross on the roof? A gilder's the guy who puts the gold on it. He worked as slowly as possible, trying to keep an eye on the place, but two days was as long as he was able to stretch it. And he really couldn't see anything from up there anyhow, except the monks — the local, talking kind — walking around in the garden.'

'Then it's up to us, Fink,' the agent in charge said. 'When troops fail, the commanding officer goes into the line, right?'

'Right, Chief,' deputy agent-in-charge Finklestein said. 'What have you got in mind?'

Forty-five minutes later, a panel truck pulled up in front of the Chancellory of the Diocese of Greater Miami and the Florida Keys. A magnetic sign was stuck on each door:

'GREATER MIAMI BIBLE SUPPLY COMPANY'
BIBLES TO THE TRADE
WHOLESALE & RETAIL
'WE WILL NOT BE UNDERSOLD'
'BEWARE OF IMITATIONS'

Two bearded men wearing coveralls got out and, after looking nervously up and down the street, walked across it and up the walk to the door of the Chancellory of the diocese of Greater Miami and the Florida Keys. One of them, who was carrying a small cardboard box, pushed the doorbell. Inside, they could hear chimes playing 'The Bells of St. Mary's.' In a moment the door was opened by a gentleman in clerical collar. He did not, the agent in charge realized immediately, look anywhere near as friendly as Bing Crosby, and he was several sizes larger.

'Good morning, sir,' the agent in charge said. 'Do I have the honour of addressing His Excellency the Bishop of Greater Miami and the Florida Keys, also known as O'Grogarty, Patrick Michael?'

'No,' the large, ugly, rather unfriendly gentleman in the clerical collar said. 'Whatever you guys are selling, we don't want any.'

'Actually,' deputy agent-in-charge Finklestein said, 'we're not *selling* anything.'

'What's in the box?'

'A Bible,' the agent in charge said, hastily tearing the box open. 'See for yourself. Now what could be more innocent, I ask you, than a Bible?'

The large gentleman in the clerical collar took the Bible, examined the title page, and then held it by the binding and shook it, as if he expected something to fall out. Nothing did – except the sales slip from Sears, Roebuck, which the agent

111

in charge had neglected to remove when, thirty minutes before, on the way over, he had purchased the Bible.

'What am I supposed to do with this?' the larger clerical gentleman asked.

'It's a present for Bishop O'Grogarty,' Finklestein said.

'From who?'

'From an admirer who wishes to remain anonymous,' the agent in charge said, smoothly. 'Now, if you will just tell the bishop we're here, so we can get his signature on the receipt, we'll be on our way, and the bishop can start reading his nice, new Bible. You'll notice that it has four-colour pictures of all the saints and people like that, and a place for him to put down the names of his children.'

'What are you two creeps up to?'

'Why, nothing at all, nothing at all,' the agent in charge said. 'Forgive me for saying this, Father, but you seem unduly suspicious for a man of the cloth.'

'*I* seem suspicious? Now, why should *I* seem suspicious? Because two creeps show up here in beards, the moustache of one of which has come unglued, with a Sears, Roebuck edition of the St. James Version of the Bible for the bishop? Now, why should that make me suspicious?'

'I can't imagine,' the agent in charge said.

'Is there something we should know about St. James?' Finklestein asked. 'Is he in hot water with the Vatican or something?'

'I wouldn't go so far as to say that,' the priest said. 'Let me just say that we prefer the Douay version around here.'

'You should have checked that out, Finklestein,' the agent in charge said.

'Don't try to blame me, Chief. *We* only use the first part of that book. *You're* the one who should know. You're always bragging about being a Baptist elder.'

The agent in charge looked thoughtful a moment, then looked up at the priest.

'Are you, sir, going to tell the bishop we are here?'

'No,' the priest said succinctly.

'In that case,' the agent in charge said, ripping off his beard with his left hand as he reached for his official F.B.I. badge and credentials with the others, 'we must take you into our confidence. . . .'

The priest slammed the door in his face.

'Now what, Chief?' Finklestein asked. 'Shall we break the door down?'

'Of course not,' the agent in charge said. 'Only Alcohol, Tobacco & Firearms can go around smashing down doors and wrecking places without a warrant. We have to be paragons of legal and moral prudence in our work. What we'll do is go by the phone company and put a tap on their line.'

'Good thinking, Chief,' Finklestein said.

'You don't get to be an agent in charge by being a dum-dum, Fink, remember that,' the agent in charge said. He handed Mr. Finklestein the Bible. 'On the way, we'll stop by Sears and get our money back. They sold us the wrong one, anyway.'

Inside the chancellory, the large priest, who was in fact a monsignor and chancellor of the diocese, watched as the two gentlemen walked back to their van, got in, and drove away.

He lit a cigar, took a couple of thoughtful puffs, and then went to his desk and reached for the phone.

When a pleasant female voice came on the line, he said, 'This is Monsignor Moran in Miami. Is Monsignor Clancy available?' The monsignor was. 'Hey, Jack, Bob Moran in Miami. How's tricks?'

'Rather calm for a change, Bob. What's on your mind?'

'Well, the boss told me, just before he went to Europe, that if anything came up I couldn't handle, I should get in touch with your boss.'

'He's out playing golf, Bob. Is there anything you can tell me? Anything I can do?'

'Couple of things I can't understand,' Monsignor Moran said. 'For one thing, I can't find the bishop in Paris. I've tried three times. The hotel says that he went out at about eight

113

o'clock last night, bound for the opera, and hasn't been seen since.'

'How odd! And what else?'

'You won't believe this, Jack, but so help me, I haven't so much as sniffed a cork since the boss left. But just now two weirdos with glued-on beards came knocking at the door. They had a Sears, Roebuck edition of the St. James Version of the Bible, and they wanted to give it to the bishop.'

'Well, he should be cleared to read it. What's wrong with that?'

'They wanted him to sign for it.'

'We have them here all the time. Two weeks after you sign for something, you get a coupon book from the Friendly Finance Company. You either send them a dollar a week for the rest of your life, or they'll send the sheriff to foreclose on you.'

'Well, it's strange enough that it bothers me, Jack. That's why I called.'

'I can't help you with the Bible, but I do have a . . . an acquaintance . . . in Paris I can call about the bishop.'

'Who's that?'

'Well, I'd rather not say, Bob, but I think I can get results.'

'I understand perfectly, Jack,' Monsignor Moran said. 'We all have our anonymous friends here and there to call on when we need them, don't we?'

'I'll call him right away and get back to you, Bob.'

'Appreciate it, Jack. Any time I can do anything for you . . .'

'Happy to be of service, Bob,' Monsignor Clancy said. He broke the connection with his finger, then dialled the overseas operator. Then, suddenly changing his mind, he broke the connection, too, and dialled another number. He knew this one by heart, from pained memory.

'God Is Love in All Forms Christian Church, Incorporated,' a lilting voice of indeterminate sexual persuasion announced. '*Good* morning!'

'Good morning,' Monsignor Clancy said. 'May I speak with the Rev. Mother Emeritus Wilson, please?'

'Might I be so bold as to inquire who with such a sexy, *masculine* voice is calling?'

'Tell her Jack Clancy,' the monsignor replied.

'Perhaps *I* might be of service, Jack. Is there anything at all, *any*thing at *all*, that I could do for you?'

'Just let me talk to the Reverend Mother Emeritus,' Monsignor Clancy said, reminding himself to judge not, lest ye be judged, and that Michelangelo himself had been a little light on his feet and yet had rendered the Church great service.

'Well,' the voice replied, 'she's busy, busy, busy, but I'll tell her you're on the line. No promises or anything.'

'Thank you,' the monsignor said.

In a moment a warm female voice came on the line.

'Jackie-Baby, what a pleasant surprise!' she said. 'What can l'il ol' Reverend Mother do for you?'

'I need a little favour, Hot Lips,' the monsignor said.

'Name it,' she replied immediately. 'I mean, what chance has ecumenism got if we don't help each other out?'

The monsignor felt that there was such a thing as pushing churchly union too far, but he said nothing.

'Have you got friends in Paris?' the monsignor asked.

'Have I got friends in Paris? Is the Pope ... certainly, I have friends in Paris. What's the problem?'

'Probably nothing,' the monsignor said. 'But the Chancellor of the Diocese of Greater Miami and the Florida Keys, Bob Moran – he's an old friend of mine – just called.'

'And?'

'It seems his bishop is lost in Paris.'

'Well, Jack, you know how it is,' the Reverend Mother said. 'Maybe he *wants* to be lost. All work and no play, as I always say.'

'It's nothing like that, I'm sure,' the monsignor said firmly. 'He left his hotel in the cardinal-archbishop's car for the opera, and that's the last anyone's heard of him.' After a moment, he added, 'He was in his bishop's formal dress, Hot Lips.'

115

'Well, that rules out, I suppose, a night on the town,' the Reverend Mother said. 'Let me have his name, Jackie-Baby, and I'll get right on it.'

'Patrick Michael O'Grogarty,' Monsignor Clancy said.

'Boy, you really have it sewn up, don't you? You're as bad as the New York Police Force.'

'I don't know what you mean,' Monsignor Clancy said.

'I'd hate to be an ordinary priest named Goldberg trying to get to be a monsignor, that's what I mean, Jackie-Baby,' she said. 'But no offence. I'll get back to you.'

'I'd be grateful,' Monsignor Clancy said. Once he'd hung up, he had, briefly, second thoughts about involving Hot Lips and the God Is Love, etc., in the problem, but quickly realized it was better than calling up the Cardinal-Archbishop of Paris and asking if he'd happened to run across a lost bishop.

Rev. Mother Emeritus Wilson pushed the button on her intercom.

'Jimmy, be a dear and get His Royal Highness on the horn for me, will you?'

'Which royal highness is that, Reverend Mother? The short fat one in Paris, or that *gorgeous* hunk of Arabian *stallion* in Abzug?'

'The Paris one,' she replied.

Five minutes later the intercom buzzed.

'Paris on three, Reverend Mother, but not His Royal Short Fat Highness.'

'Rev. Mother Emeritus Margaret H. W. Wilson here,' Hot Lips said to the phone. 'Who's this?'

'I have the honour to be Abdullah Yacim ben Mussid, first under-secretary and chief of missions of the Parisian embassy of His Most Islamic Majesty, the King of Hussid.'

'You're the great big one with the scar on his left cheek and those sexy dark eyes?'

'I don't believe I've had the pleasure, Madame,' the chief of mission said somewhat icily.

116

'Oh, of *course* you have,' the Reverend Mother Emeritus said. 'This is Hot Lips, Abdullah-Baby.'

'Oh, Mademoiselle *Hot Lips!* Why didn't you say so?'

'Just to keep the record straight, Abdullah-Baby, that's *Reverend Mother Emeritus* Hot Lips. But you may, of course, just call me Hot Lips.'

'How may His Majesty's embassy be of service to you, Hot Lips?'

'I was hoping to talk to Hassan,' she said.

'His Royal Highness, Reverend Mother Hot Lips, as I thought you knew, is en route to Miami, Florida.'

'I knew, of course, but that's not until day after tomorrow. You mean he's left already?'

'He went via Prudhoe Bay, Alaska. Something to do with picking up Colonel Horsey and François Mulligan, I believe. Is there any way I might be of service?'

'As a matter of fact, Abdullah-Baby . . .'

CHAPTER ELEVEN

'You sent for me, Sheikh Abdullah?' inquired Mustapha ben Shazam, *chef du protocole* and chief of security of the Royal Hussidic Embassy.

'You are aware of the close relationship between His Royal Highness and the infidel woman known as Reverend Mother Hot Lips?'

'Painfully aware, Sheikh Abdullah.'

'And of the standing order around here that whatever Reverend Mother Hot Lips wants, Reverend Mother gets?'

'Even more painfully, Sheikh Abdullah.'

'She's thrown us a real can of worms this time, Sheikh Mustapha,' the chief of mission said.

'Oh?'

'Somewhere in Paris is another infidel, an Irish infidel, an official of the infidel church . . . a bishop, I believe. The name is Patrick Michael O'Grogarty. We are to find him and send him home. He is lost.'

'Maybe he wants to be lost,' Sheikh Mustapha said, winking and twirling his moustache.

'I don't care if he wants to be lost or not. If the Reverend Mother Emeritus Hot Lips wants him sent home, he gets sent home.'

'Your wish, of course, is my command,' Sheikh Mustapha replied.

'Where will you start?'

'I will drop by the Foreign Ministry, pick up the foreign minister, and take him along with me to the headquarters of the Gerdarmerie Nationale.'

'In that case, I'll go with you,' the chief of mission said. 'Call the airport and have them make a plane ready.'

'Your wish, of course, is my command,' Sheikh Mustapha said again.

'Keep that in mind, Mustapha,' the chief of mission said.

The commandant of the Paris Region, Gendarmerie Nationale, was surprised to see His Excellency the Foreign Minister of the French Republic come marching into his headquarters. A bureaucrat of such exalted status as the foreign minister rarely made personal visits to the Gendarmerie Nationale. Usually, the commandant was summoned to the Foreign Ministry and told to come in an unmarked car and enter by the rear door. Or some minor underling would appear at the Gendarmerie Nationale. But rarely a high-ranking official, and absolutely never the foreign minister himself.

But when His Excellency introduced His Excellency Sheikh Abdullah Yacim ben Mussid, chief of mission of the Royal Hussidic Embassy, and his *chef du protocole*, he of course understood. After all, the Sheikhdom of Hussid supplied thirty-eight per cent of the petroleum needs of *la belle* France, and Air Hussid, of all the world's airlines, was the only one that had purchased Le Discorde aircraft – or could afford to fly them. That explained a good deal. *La belle* France was willing, even eager, to do practically anything to sell Le Discorde aircraft; the commandant himself had learned of an offer by the interior minister to have the Eiffel Tower turned into an outdoor billboard spelling out ALL THE WAY WITH T.W.A. if that airline would purchase, on a money-back guarantee basis, just *one* of the droop-nosed flying machines.

'And how,' the commandant said, rising to his feet and oozing Gallic charm from every sweaty pore, 'may the Gendarmerie Nationale be of service to your distinguished self, M'sieu le Foreign Minister, and your handsome and charming friends?'

'Sheikh Abdullah seeks,' the foreign minister said – 'which is to say, of course, that the source of thirty-eight per cent of our petroleum seeks – an American prelate of the Church who is missing in Paris.'

119

'Sheikh Abdullah,' the commandant said, 'put your mind to rest. If your distinguished prelate friend is in Paris, the Gendarmerie Nationale will find him! Would you by any chance have a description, or any other sort of a clue, on which we can build our search?'

'His name is O'Grogarty, Patrick Michael,' Sheikh Abdullah replied.

'Isn't that interesting,' the commandant said. 'We have a chap in our custody with a name very much like that: Patrick Michael O'Grogarty.'

'Perhaps it is the same man. The names are similar.'

'Oh, this couldn't be your prelate. This one, we feel, is a high-ranking officer of the Irish Republican Army.'

'How can you be so sure that he's not our man?' Sheikh Mustapha asked.

'I wouldn't repeat the language he's been using,' the commandant said. 'Prelates don't talk like that.'

'We of the Royal Hussidic Security Service never leave a stone unturned,' Sheikh Mustapha said. 'I would like to see this chap.' He paused, twirled his moustache, and added: 'Alone.'

'I will go with you, Mustapha,' Sheikh Abdullah said.

'Your wish is my command,' Sheikh Mustapha said.

Three minutes later, a heavy steel door in sub-basement three of the detention facility of the Paris Region, Gendarmerie Nationale (known popularly as the 'New Bastille'), was pushed creakingly open. One middle-aged Irishman and two middle-aged Hussidians stared at each other with undisguised interest.

'Who are you?' Patrick Michael O'Grogarty asked.

'It is we who will ask the questions, and you who will answer them,' Sheikh Mustapha said. 'Who are *you*?'

'I am Patrick Michael O'Grogarty, Bishop of Greater Miami and the Florida Keys.'

'Ha!' Sheikh Mustapha said.

'Ha!' Sheikh Abdullah said.

'Why won't anyone *believe* me?' Patrick Michael O'Grogarty asked rhetorically.

'Let me put it to you this way,' Sheikh Mustapha said. 'If you came across, in the third sub-basement of the New Bastille, a red-faced Irisher wearing nothing but a T-shirt and polka-dot shorts, and he said he was the Bishop of Greater Miami and the Florida Keys, would *you* believe him?'

'They took my clothing . . . brand-new clothing, purchased only last week in Rome . . . and left me here like this,' Patrick Michael O'Grogarty replied.

'Just like that? Just snatched you off the street, stripped you, and threw you in the slammer? With no reason?' Sheikh Mustapha asked, dripping sarcasm from every sibilant syllable.

'A singer told them to,' Patrick Michael O'Grogarty said. 'A singer accused me of singing off-key, of being drunk on stage, and of stealing a costume.'

'A singer? A *singer?* You expect me to believe that?'

'A great big man, with a beard. He was attempting to pick a fistfight with a priest, and when I tried to stop the fight, the next thing I knew, I was being grabbed by the cops.'

'A great big singer? With a beard?'

'Oh, I know you won't believe me, but it's the truth!'

Sheikh Mustapha and Sheikh Abdullah exchanged significant looks.

'Go get the foreign minister, Mustapha,' Sheikh Abdullah said.

'Your wish is my command,' Sheikh Mustapha replied, bowing deeply. He turned toward the door of the dungeon. 'Hey, Foreign Minister!'

The foreign minister and the commandant came into the dungeon.

'Yes, Your Excellencies?' the foreign minister said.

'I wish to inform you, sir,' Sheikh Abdullah said, 'as chief of mission of the Parisian embassy of His Most Islamic Majesty, the King of Hussid (may his tribe increase), that this red-faced Irish is now under the protection of the Royal Hussidic Embassy.'

121

'I don't quite follow you, Your Excellency,' the foreign minister said.

'Unless you want to ride to work on a bicycle, you'd better not,' Sheikh Abdullah said. 'Come along, Irisher!'

'You mean, I'm getting out?'

'Not only are you getting out, red-faced Irisher infidel, you are, through the boundless mercy of His Most Islamic Majesty's Parisian embassy, going home.'

'I don't *want* to go home,' Patrick Michael O'Grogarty said. 'I want to go back to my hotel.'

'Don't press your luck, infidel,' Sheikh Mustapha said.

FROM F.B.I. MIAMI
TO F.B.I. WASHINGTON

REFERENCE YOUR TELETYPE RE: PATRICK MICHAEL O'GROGARTY, ALLEGEDLY BISHOP OF GREATER MIAMI AND THE FLORIDA KEYS.

1. THE AGENT IN CHARGE HAS PERSONALLY ASSUMED COMMAND OF THE INVESTIGATION, ASSISTED BY DEPUTY AGENT-IN-CHARGE LLEWELLYN FINKLESTEIN.

2. FOLLOWING UNUSUALLY SUSPICIOUS BEHAVIOUR ON PART OF INDIVIDUAL DRESSED AS PRIEST AND REPRESENTING HIMSELF AS MEMBER OF STAFF, DIOCESE OF GREATER MIAMI AND THE FLORIDA KEYS, TELEPHONIC SURVEILLANCE WAS PLACED ON PREMISES ALLEGEDLY THOSE OF DIOCESE OF GREATER MIAMI AND THE FLORIDA KEYS.

3. A TOTAL OF FOUR HUNDRED ELEVEN (411) TELEPHONIC COMMUNICATIONS TO THE PREMISES ALLEGEDLY THOSE OF DIOCESE OF GREATER MIAMI AND THE FLORIDA KEYS WERE INTERCEPTED, RECORDED, AND ANALYSED BY THE AGENT IN CHARGE HIMSELF, WITH SOME ASSISTANCE FROM DEPUTY AGENT-IN-CHARGE L. FINKLESTEIN.

4. TWO COMMUNICATIONS APPEAR TO HAVE SOME BEARING ON THIS CASE. VERBATIM TRANSCRIPTS FOLLOW.

ANSWERING PARTY AT PREMISES ALLEGEDLY THOSE OF
DIOCESE OF GREATER MIAMI AND THE FLORIDA KEYS
HEREINAFTER REFERRED TO AS AP. CALLING PARTY
HEREINAFTER REFERRED TO AS CP.

AP: CHANCELLORY OF THE DIOCESE OF GREATER
MIAMI AND THE FLORIDA KEYS.

CP: MONSIGNOR CLANCY CALLING FOR MONSIGNOR
MORAN.

AP: ONE MOMENT PLEASE, MONSIGNOR.

AP: MONSIGNOR MORAN.

CP: JACK CLANCY, BOB.

AP: I'VE BEEN EXPECTING YOUR CALL.

CP: I JUST HAD A CALL FROM HOT LIPS.

AP: FROM WHO?

CP: MY CONTACT.

AP: I THOUGHT YOU SAID 'HOT LIPS.'

CP: YOUR BISHOP IS ON HIS WAY HOME.

AP: EVERYTHING IS ALL RIGHT, THEN?

CP: LET'S SAY EVERYTHING HAS APPARENTLY TURNED
OUT ALL RIGHT.

AP: JACK, YOU SEEM TO BE BEATING AROUND THE BUSH.
IS THERE SOMETHING I SHOULD KNOW? SOMETHING
YOU KNOW AND DON'T WANT TO TELL ME?

CP: IT'S SORT OF DELICATE, BOB. I DON'T REALLY
KNOW HOW TO TELL YOU THIS.

AP: TELL ME WHAT?

CP: WELL, ACCORDING TO THE INFORMATION I HAVE,
BOB, IT SEEMS YOUR BISHOP WAS IN THE SLAMMER.

AP: MY BISHOP? IN THE SLAMMER? THAT'S OUT OF THE
QUESTION, IMPOSSIBLE!

CP: PROBABLY SOME SIMPLE MISUNDERSTANDING. ALL
I CAN TELL YOU IS WHAT I WAS TOLD.

AP: WHAT, PRECISELY, WERE YOU TOLD?

CP: MY CONTACT HERE TOLD ME THAT HER CONTACT IN
PARIS HAD JUST TELEPHONED TO SAY THEY FOUND

YOUR BISHOP WEARING NOTHING BUT HIS UNDER-
WEAR, IN THE NEW BASTILLE, BUT NOT TO WORRY,
THAT THEY HAD SPRUNG HIM, GIVEN HIM SOME-
THING TO WEAR, AND WERE SENDING HIM HOME.

AP: DID YOU SAY 'HER'? YOU WANT TO TELL ME WHO
YOUR CONTACT IS?

CP: I DON'T REALLY THINK YOU OR YOUR BISHOP
WOULD WANT TO KNOW, BOB. LET ME SAY THAT
SHE'S A FRIEND OF MY ARCHBISHOP AND CAN BE
TRUSTED.

AP: SHE DIDN'T SAY WHY MY BISHOP WAS IN THE
SLAMM — WHY HE HAD BEEN UNJUSTLY ARRESTED?

CP: SHE DIDN'T HAVE ALL THE DETAILS. BUT AP-
PARENTLY HE'D HAD A FEW TOO MANY.

AP: ARE YOU IMPLYING WHAT I THINK YOU'RE IMPLY-
ING?

CP: ONE OF THE CHARGES AGAINST HIM WAS COMMIT-
TING AN OFFENCE AGAINST THE PEACE AND
DIGNITY OF PARIS BY APPEARING DRUNK ON THE
STAGE OF THE PARIS OPERA AND SINGING OUT OF
TUNE.

AP: OH, MY —!

CP: BUT THE CHARGES HAVE BEEN DROPPED, BOB, SO
NOT TO WORRY.

AP: WHAT WERE THE OTHER CHARGES?

CP: YOU DON'T REALLY WANT TO KNOW, DO YOU, BOB?

AP: I DON'T WANT TO KNOW, JACK. BUT I THINK IT'S MY
DUTY TO FIND OUT.

CP: WELL, THERE WAS SOMETHING ABOUT STEALING A
COSTUME.

AP: WHAT KIND OF A COSTUME?

CP: THEY DIDN'T SAY.

AP: ANYTHING ELSE?

CP: NOT MUCH.

AP: TELL ME, JACK.

CP: RESISTING ARREST. BUT THEY'VE ALL BEEN
DROPPED, BOB, AND HE'S ON HIS WAY HOME.

AP: CAN I ASK YOU SOMETHING, JACK?

CP: SURE, BOB. ANYTHING AT ALL.

AP: IF THIS HAD HAPPENED TO YOUR ARCHBISHOP, HOW WOULD YOU HAVE HANDLED IT?

CP: I REALLY CAN'T IMAGINE MY ARCHBISHOP GETTING PLASTERED AND SINGING OUT OF TUNE ON THE STAGE OF THE PARIS OPERA, BOB.

AP: THAT WAS A REALLY ROTTEN THING TO SAY, JACK.

CP: OR RUNNING AROUND IN HIS UNDERWEAR IN PUBLIC, EITHER.

AP: I THINK YOU REALLY THINK THIS IS FUNNY.

CP: WELL, YOU HAVE TO ADMIT, IT IS A TRIFLE HUMOROUS.

AP: GOOD NIGHT, MONSIGNOR CLANCY.

CP: COME ON, BOB. DON'T GET SORE AT ME ... I'LL BE DAMNED, HE HUNG UP.

CALL ONE ENDED HERE.

B. CALL NUMBER TWO:

AP: CHANCELLORY OF THE DIOCESE OF GREATER MIAMI AND THE FLORIDA KEYS.

CP: LET ME SPEAK TO MONSIGNOR MORAN.

AP: I'M SORRY, SIR, MONSIGNOR MORAN IS NOT AVAILABLE AT THE MOMENT.

CP: WHAT DO YOU MEAN, HE'S NOT AVAILABLE?

AP: WHAT'S THE MATTER, YOU DEAF OR SOMETHING? I MEAN HE'S NOT AVAILABLE. THAT MEANS YOU CAN'T TALK TO HIM.

CP: I HAVE TO TALK TO HIM.

AP: MAY I SUGGEST, SIR, THAT YOU CALL BACK IN THE MORNING AND ASK FOR SISTER MARY MAGDALENE? SISTER IS THE MONSIGNOR'S SECRETARY, AND SHE MIGHT BE ABLE TO HELP YOU.

CP: HE'S ASLEEP, ISN'T HE? I MEAN, HE DIDN'T GO TO THE MOVIES OR ANYTHING?

AP: IF IT MAKES YOU ANY HAPPIER, YES, MONSIGNOR MORAN IS ASLEEP. AND YOU WOULDN'T WANT TO DISTURB HIM, WOULD YOU?

CP: WAKE HIM UP! WAKE HIM UP!

AP: OH, I'M SORRY, SIR. THAT'S OUT OF THE QUESTION.

CP: THIS IS AN EMERGENCY!

AP: IN THAT CASE, SIR, I'LL PUT YOU THROUGH TO SISTER MARY MAGDALENE AT THE CONVENT. SHE ALWAYS STAYS UP TO WATCH JOHNNY CARSON.

CP: NO! I DON'T WANT TO SPEAK TO SISTER MARY MAGDALENE. I WANT TO SPEAK TO MONSIGNOR MORAN.

AP: AS I'VE TOLD YOU BEFORE, SIR, THAT'S IMPOSSIBLE. THE MONSIGNOR NEEDS HIS REST.

CP: DON'T MAKE ME LAUGH! I'M THE ONE WHO NEEDS HIS REST.

AP: IF THERE'S NOTHING ELSE, SIR, I MUST BREAK OFF THE CONNECTION.

CP: LISTEN TO ME, YOUNG WOMAN, IF YOU DON'T WAKE MONSIGNOR MORAN UP AND TELL HIM HIS FRIEND PATRICK MICHAEL IS ON THE PHONE, HE'S NOT GOING TO LIKE IT.

AP: THOSE ARE THE FIRST NAMES OF OUR BELOVED BISHOP. I HOPE FOR YOUR SAKE THAT YOU'RE NOT TAKING THEM IN VAIN.

CP: JUST TELL HIM, FOR THE LOVE OF GOD, JUST TELL HIM!

AP: VERY WELL. . . .

AP(2):   MONSIGNOR MORAN.

AP: MONSIGNOR, I'M TERRIBLY SORRY TO BOTHER YOU AFTER YOU'VE RETIRED, BUT THERE'S THIS PERSISTENT CHARACTER ON THE LINE WHO INSISTS ON SPEAKING TO YOU. HE SAYS HIS NAME IS PATRICK MICHAEL. I TRIED TO GET HIM TO TALK TO SISTER MARY MAGDALENE, BUT HE INSISTS ON SPEAKING TO YOU.

AP(2):   YOU JUST TELL MR. MICHAEL TO CALL BACK

DURING OFFICE HOURS — WAIT A MINUTE. PUT HIM
THROUGH, OPERATOR.

CP: BOB?

AP(2): IS THIS WHO I THINK IT IS?

CP: NO NAMES, BOB.

AP(2): YES, SIR, YOUR EXCELLENCY.

CP: GO EASY ON THAT 'YOUR EXCELLENCY' BUSINESS,
TOO, BOB.

AP(2): YES, SIR.

CP: NOW LISTEN CAREFULLY, BOB. I WANT YOU TO GO
DOWN TO THE GARAGE AND GET OUT THE LIM-
OUSINE. I WANT YOU TO DRIVE IT YOURSELF, AND
BEFORE YOU START OUT, CLOSE ALL THOSE LITTLE
CURTAINS IN THE BACK, THE ONES THAT KEEP
PEOPLE FROM LOOKING IN. THAT'S VERY IMPOR-
TANT.

AP(2): YES, SIR.

CP: THEN COME OUT TO THE AIRPORT AND GET ME.

AP(2): YES, SIR. RIGHT AWAY. YOU'LL BE IN THE V.I.P.
LOUNGE AS USUAL?

CP: NO. I'LL BE BEHIND THE 'HI, MY NAME IS BOBBSIE,
FLY ME TO NEW YORK' SIGN.

AP(2): SIR?

CP: YOU KNOW THE ONE, BOB. THE BLONDE IN THE
COWBOY HAT AND ALMOST NOTHING ELSE.

AP(2): I'LL LEAVE RIGHT AWAY, SIR. I HOPE I'LL BE
ABLE TO FIND YOU ALL RIGHT, SIR.

CP: ABOUT THAT, BOB.

AP(2): SIR?

CP: WHEN YOU GET TO THE SIGN, BOB, YOU'LL SEE
SOMEONE IN FLOWING ROBES AND A BURNOOSE.

AP(2): A WHAT? FLOWING ROBES AND A WHAT?

CP: A BURNOOSE. WHAT THE ARABS WEAR ON THEIR
HEADS TO KEEP THE SUN OFF AND THE SAND OUT.

AP(2): YES, SIR, OF COURSE.

CP: IN THE STRICTEST CONFIDENCE, BOB, THAT'LL BE
ME.

127

AP(2):   SIR?
CP: JUST GET THE CAR AND COME DOWN HERE, MONSIGNOR!

CALL TWO ENDED HERE.

5. THE INVESTIGATION, INCLUDING TELEPHONIC SUR-
   VEILLANCE, WILL OF COURSE CONTINUE, UNDER THE
   PERSONAL GUIDANCE OF THE UNDERSIGNED.
6. ANALYSIS OF ALL INFORMATION GATHERED TO DATE
   INDICATES THE FOLLOWING.

A. THE LARGE GRANITE AND MARBLE BUILDING
LOCATED ADJACENT TO THE CATHEDRAL OF ST. JOHN
AND BEARING A BRASS SIGN READING 'CHANCELLORY OF
THE DIOCESE OF GREATER MIAMI AND THE FLORIDA
KEYS' IS MORE THAN LIKELY THE CHANCELLORY OF THE
DIOCESE OF GREATER MIAMI AND THE FLORIDA KEYS.

B. THE SUSPECT IDENTIFIED AS PATRICK MICHAEL
O'GROGARTY, ALLEGEDLY BISHOP OF THE DIOCESE OF
GREATER MIAMI AND THE FLORIDA KEYS –
   (1) HAS A DRINKING PROBLEM, AND/OR
   (2) IS A LITTLE FLAKY, AND/OR
   (3) HAS SECRET CONNECTIONS OF AN UNKNOWN
       NATURE WITH ONE OR MORE OF THE OIL-
       EXPORTING COUNTRIES.

7. IN COMPLIANCE WITH THE PROVISIONS OF F.B.I.
REGULATION 110.C4, 'RELATIONS WITH THE UNITED
STATES POSTAL SERVICE,' THIS OFFICE IS TODAY FOR-
WARDING, VIA UNITED PARCEL SERVICE, ONE BIBLE
(KING JAMES VERSION), WHICH IS SURPLUS TO THE NEEDS
OF THIS OFFICE AND WHICH THIS OFFICE WAS UNABLE TO
RETURN FOR CREDIT.

BIRCH BEEBE, AGENT IN CHARGE

CHAPTER TWELVE

The Baroness d'Iberville slipped into the royal cabin of the Air Hussid airplane and knelt beside one of the two beds, taking great care with the tray she carried. The tray held a silver coffee pot, a Meissen china cup and saucer, and a bottle of Courvoisier cognac.

Boris Alexandrovich Korsky-Rimsakov lay on the bed on his back, his legs spread, his arms at his sides, his mouth hanging slightly open, his eyes tightly closed. He was snoring loudly. So loudly, in fact, that a sympathetic vibration had been set up with the covering of the NO SMOKING FASTEN SEAT BELTS sign on the wall. It rattled alarmingly with every exhaled breath.

The baroness set the tray on the bedside table, carefully poured the Meissen cup half full of steaming coffee, and then uncorked the bottle of cognac. She waved the open neck of the bottle back and forth.

The massive left nostril of Boris Alexandrovich Korsky-Rimsakov twitched. Then the right nostril twitched. And finally both nostrils twitched in unison. The massive head turned toward the neck of the cognac bottle like a radar antenna locking in on an intercontinental ballistic missile. The nostrils shuddered, and one eye opened.

'Are you out of your mind?' Boris asked. 'Can't you see that I'm rooming with an archbishop? Have you no shame? No control of your baser emotions whatever?'

'The archbishop isn't here,' the baroness replied. 'He said he couldn't stand the noise in here.'

'No wonder. I've never heard a cup of coffee poured so noisily.'

'Should I put a little cognac in the coffee, *Cher* Boris?'

'Make it half and half,' he said. 'I'm a sick man.'

She poured cognac into the coffee cup, filling it. Boris took it from her and drained it in two gulps. He turned and looked out the window.

'Thank God!'

'For what?' the baroness asked.

'I had the most terrifying nightmare. I dreamed I . . . never mind. Where are we?'

'Half an hour or so from Spruce Harbour, Maine,' the baroness said.

'What the hell are we going to do in Spruce Harbour, Maine?'

'We're going to pick up Hawkeye and Trapper John,' the baroness said.

'What for?'

'To take them to Miami, Florida.'

'I've never heard of anything so idiotic!' he said. 'Whose preposterous idea was this?'

'Why, yours, of course, *Cher* Boris,' she said.

'In that case, there must be a good reason. Give me a little more of the coffee, and don't be so stingy with the brandy this time.'

Up in the front of the aircraft, where the pilots and crew usually had their parties, things were quiet and businesslike. The pilot now flying the aircraft didn't like to monkey around when he was at the controls.

The Air Hussid plane was a DC-9. Normally, his Royal Highness Prince Hassan ad Kayam travelled in a Le Discorde, but for this trip, this had been quite out of the question. For one thing, while Le Discorde aircraft flew fast, they didn't fly very far. A nonstop Paris–Prudhoe Bay, Alaska, trip was impossible. For another, Le Discorde made so much noise when landing and taking off that a coalition had been formed by various special-interest lobbies – who normally couldn't stand the sight of each other, but who had buried the hatchet briefly – to convince the United States Congress that permitting Le Discorde aircraft to land anywhere in the United States would so enrage all voters of all persuasions within one hundred miles of the field that not one person who voted to give it landing rights would ever be returned to any political office whatsoever.

Faced with what the politicians called 'the cold fact that Le Discorde poses awful threats to the environment and the mental stability of the country,' the Congress had wisely denied the aircraft landing rights anywhere in the United States. That, unfortunately, included Prudhoe Bay, Alaska.

'Boston Area Control,' the pilot of the Air Hussid DC–9 now said, 'Air Hussid Twelve at three zero thousand feet over Montreal. Estimate Spruce Harbour International in twenty-five minutes. Request permission to begin descent for approach to Spruce Harbour.'

'Air Hussid Twelve, Boston Area Control. A word to the wise, fella. We don't like wise guys. Spruce Harbour International, my eye!'

'Boston, I say again, Air Hussid Twelve requests permission to leave three zero thousand to begin approach to Spruce Harbour International.'

'Air Hussid Twelve, Boston. O.K., wise guy, you got it. Boston clears Air Hussid Twelve for descent from three zero thousand feet for approach to Spruce Harbour International. Boston advises Air Hussid Twelve we have you on radar, and you better try to get into Spruce Harbour.'

'Roger, Boston. Air Hussid Twelve leaving three zero thousand at this time,' the pilot said. He changed his radio frequency. 'Spruce Harbour International, Air Hussid Twelve.'

There was no reply.

'Spruce Harbour International, this is Air Hussid Twelve.'

'Aircraft calling Spruce Harbour International is advised that Spruce Harbour International is closed to all traffic for an indefinite period.'

'That you, Wrong Way?' the pilot of Air Hussid Twelve said.

'I hope this isn't who I think it is,' Spruce Harbour replied.

'Why, Wrong Way, why do you say that?' the pilot asked.

131

'It's not nice to lie to an archbishop, that's why,' Spruce Harbour said.

'For the time being, Wrong Way, just think of me as an ordinary pilot whose Air Transport Rating is multi-engine, unlimited horsepower,' Archbishop Mulcahy replied.* 'Air Hussid Twelve passing through two five thousand, estimate Spruce Harbour International Airport as well as the airport's chief (and only) control tower operator, was, to coin a phrase, on the horns of a dilemma.

At five minutes past eleven the previous evening, Mr. Napolitano had received a telephone call from Dr. John Francis Xavier ('Trapper John') McIntyre, who had been calling from the residence of Dr. Benjamin Franklin ('Hawkeye') Pierce.

Dr. McIntyre had informed Mr. Napolitano that they had just had a very long-distance telephone call from a Mr. B. A. Korsky-Rimsakov, and that it was their studied medical judgment that Mr. Korsky-Rimsakov had been at the grape.

'Setting new standards,' Hawkeye Pierce had chimed in on the extension phone, 'even for him. He's hallucinating. He said that he was calling from the top of the Eiffel Tower, off the top of which he was flying a paper airplane with the Painless Pole. Now you know that's absolutely beyond credibility.'

'They don't let people fly paper airplanes off the Eiffel Tower, you mean?' Wrong Way had replied.

'No,' Hawkeye had said. 'What's incredible is that he's with the Painless Pole. The Painless Pole solemnly vowed,

*His Eminence, sometime chaplain of the Cajun Air Force, had been taught to fly by the chief pilot of the aviation division, Chevaux Petroleum Corporation, International. When the Federal Aviation Administration was reluctant to issue an Air Transport Rating for DC–9 and Boeing 747 aircraft to a fifty-six-year-old pilot with two hundred thirty-five hours total flying time, His Eminence was licensed by the Royal Camel, Horse, and Aviation Ministry, Kingdom of Hussid, at the personal direction of the king himself. His Royal Highness, it will be remembered, once publicly referred to the archbishop as 'my kind of infidel.' The details may be found in M*A*S*H Goes to Las Vegas (published by Sphere Books).

many a time, that if he ever made it back to Hamtramck, it would take an earthquake to get him out. And they don't have earthquakes in Hamtramck. Riots, strikes, insurrections, sure, but no earthquakes.'

'Maybe he got married,' Wrong Way had suggested. 'That sometimes changes people.'

'My God!' Trapper John had said. 'The Lindbergh of Maine may be onto something!'

'Now listen to me, Wrong Way,' Hawkeye Pierce had said sternly. 'If, within the next seventy-two hours, any airplane bigger than Stanley K. Warczinski's Piper Cub asks for permission to land at Spruce Harbour, you tell them the field is closed for an indefinite period.'

'I can't do that, Hawkeye,' Wrong Way, a faithful, if part-time, employee of the Federal Aviation Administration had replied. 'It's against Federal regulations.'

'The Hotsy-Totsy Club, 111 South Maple Street, Bangor,' Trapper John had said.

'Miss Lotsa Bazoom,' Hawkeye had said.

'It's closed, it's closed,' Mr. Napolitano had quickly replied. . . .

Mr. Napolitano, attending the state convention of the Loyal Sons of Italy, held six months before in Bangor, Maine, had dallied for several hours at the Hotsy-Totsy Club and Massage Parlour at 111 South Maple Street. Certain photographs of Mr. Napolitano and the star *chanteuse* and masseuse, Miss Lotsa Bazoom, taken while she was toning up Mr. Napolitano's muscles, had shortly thereafter come onto the market.

Mr. Napolitano, whose expenses had exceeded the $37.50 Mrs. Napolitano had allowed him for the convention, had been in no position, money-wise, to purchase the photographs. At that point, Miss Bazoom and her employer, one Duke Jones, had, out of the goodness of their hearts, offered to show the photographs to Mrs. Napolitano and ask her if she wouldn't like to purchase them for the family album.

Mr. Napolitano had then telephoned Dr. Pierce in an

133

attempt to float an instant emergency loan. Dr. Pierce had rather sternly told him that he made it a practice never to loan money to purchase naughty photographs. He had, however, made a telephone call to a friend of a friend. Shortly thereafter, the Hotsy-Totsy Club and Massage Parlour had been visited by eight very large state troopers, who had suggested to Miss Bazoom and Mr. Jones that they would be far, far happier in far-off Montreal, and that, since they would want to be able to travel swiftly, they would have to simply abandon their collection of art photographs.

The state trooper sergeant and Doctors Pierce and McIntyre had had many a merry chuckle as they viewed the photographs. They really had had no idea how well massage had caught on among the upper crust of politicians in Maine, or, to judge from the smiles on the politicians' faces, what a pleasant experience it could be. As a small memento of the incident, Dr. McIntyre had kept some photographs of Miss Bazoom working, as it were, on the Honourable Moosenose Bartlett, Mayor of Spruce Harbour, and Dr. Pierce had kept the set of six eight-by-ten glossy photographs of Miss Bazoom and Wrong Way Napolitano.

Neither healer had ever had any trouble thereafter getting airline reservations on even the shortest of notice; and, since they had come to Mr. Napolitano's aid, their baggage had never been so much as rudely jostled, much less scratched or sent to Karachi, Pakistan, in error.

'Air Hussid passing through two zero thousand,' His Eminence said. 'Estimate Spruce Harbour International in one five minutes.'

Wrong Way Napolitano bit the bullet. He reached for the telephone and dialled a number from memory.

'Wrong Way, Miz Pierce,' he said when that lady had answered. 'The Doc there?'

'No, he's at the hospital. Anything I can do?'

Wrong Way had a sudden inspiration. 'How do you Protestants feel about lying to a Catholic archbishop?' he asked — and then recognized that he had been merely chasing a wisp of hope. 'Forget it,' he said. 'Thanks anyway.' He hung up and dialled another number from memory.

'Spruce Harbour Medical Centre.'

'This is the Federal Aviation Administration calling for Dr. Benjamin F. Pierce,' he said as officiously as he could.

'Hawkeye's in conference with Trapper John, Wrong Way,' the operator said. 'Is it important enough to disturb him in there?'

'It's an emergency,' Wrong Way said. 'Put me through.'

'This better be an emergency,' the familiar voice of Hawkeye Pierce said a moment later. 'I am in conference with Dr. McIntyre.'

'I hope he made you a strong drink, Hawkeye,' Wrong Way said. 'You ain't gonna like what I'm about to tell you.'

'It's that male model from the airport,' Hawkeye said, loud enough for Wrong Way to hear, although the comment was ostensibly directed to John Francis Xavier McIntyre, M.D., F.A.C.S. 'Do you think the bad news he's about to tell us is going to be anything like the bad news he's going to find at home after the good Mrs. Napolitano gets her illustrated how-to-do-it course in the fine points of massage?'

'Hawkeye, you wouldn't!' Wrong Way moaned.

'Not unless you let an airplane carrying Boris Alexandrovich Korsky-Rimsakov land at Spruce Harbour International, I won't.'

'How about a plane with His Eminence John Patrick Mulcahy, Archbishop of Swengchan?' Wrong Way asked desperately.

'That's a plane of a different colour,' Hawkeye replied. 'You mean, the archbishop's coming here?'

'He's about fifteen . . . no, twelve . . . minutes out.'

'That's supposed to be bad news?'

'You said that I was to say the airport was closed, period, for an indefinite period.'

'Wrong Way, shame on you!' Hawkeye said. 'Did you really think I would risk the wrath of the Vatican itself by denying one of its most distinguished archbishops, theologians, and all around good guys landing privileges at your dinky little airfield? The moment His Eminence is on the ground, please assure him that Dr. McIntyre and I are rushing to meet him.'

'I thought you'd like to know,' Wrong Way said. He did not think this was the right moment, so to speak, to inform Dr. Pierce that the airplane which His Eminence was flying was also carrying Boris Alexandrovich Korsky-Rimsakov. . . .

Dr. Pierce hung up the telephone.

'We are saved,' he said to Dr. McIntyre. 'Considering the circumstances this must be considered as help from up there.' He pointed skyward, looking a bit pious.

'You mean,' Dr. McIntyre said, his tone of voice suggesting that he didn't dare quite believe what he was hearing, 'you mean to suggest there is the slightest possibility that we will be denied the pleasure of listening to Miss Strumfeather's lecture?'*

'Ask yourself, Trapper, who is the only one of our boon companions from our years of service to our country whom both your wife-and-helpmeet and my wife-and-helpmeet admire?'

'I was about to say Radar O'Reilly,' Trapper John replied, 'but you said "admire." That means you are referring to His Eminence John Patrick Mulcahy, Archbishop of Swengchan.'

'None other,' Dr. Pierce replied, reaching for the telephone. 'Mary,' he said a moment later, 'this is your loving husband and the father of your children. I'm afraid I have bad news.'

'You're going to the P.T.A., Hawkeye, and that's it!'

---

*Miss Heloise Strumfeather, A.B., M.A., Ph.D. (Ed.), of the Maine State Parent-Teacher Association's lecture bureau, was scheduled to deliver herself of a speech entitled 'Sticky Fingers. The Joys of Finger-Painting with Your Children, in Theory and in Practice' that very evening. Mesdames Pierce and McIntyre were co-chairpersons of the 'Make Sure Hubby Comes Committee,' which was even worse.

'Whatever you say, of course, my dear, even if that will make me hurt the sensitive feelings of that distinguished prelate, His Eminence John Patrick Mulcahy, sometimes known as the Pope's strong right arm.'

'What about him?' Mary Pierce demanded somewhat suspiciously.

'His Eminence, out of the goodness of his heart, has graciously decided to stop right here in Spruce Harbour for a minute or two, pausing en route to only God knows where, to see us. Of course, if you insist that I go listen to Miss Strumfeather, your wish, my dear, as always, will be obeyed in both letter and spirit.'

'If you think, Hawkeye,' Mary Pierce said, 'that you're going to get out of the P.T.A. by sneaking onto the archbishop's airplane, think again. I'll meet you at the airport.'

'Splendid, splendid!' Hawkeye replied. 'And why don't you pick up Lucinda on your way? I know the archbishop would love to see her, too.' He had a second thought. 'If you can do so tactfully, Mary, see if you can get Lucinda to wear something other than her International Distress Orange bikini, will you? His Eminence, of course, doesn't mind, but he probably has the monsignor with him, and the monsignor blushes so painfully.' He then took the telephone from his ear and looked at John McIntyre curiously. 'Trapper, would you believe that Mary hung up on me?'

'What's wrong with my wife's bikini?' Trapper John snarled in reply.

'I think we'd better be going,' Hawkeye replied.

Meanwhile, back at Spruce Harbour International, Wrong Way Napolitano had had another thought. If there were official personages present, neither Hawkeye nor Trapper John would be likely to inflict bodily injury upon his person upon learning that Mr. Korsky-Rimsakov had indeed landed in Spruce Harbour. He therefore telephoned the Bide-A-While Pool Hall-Ladies Served Fresh Lobsters & Clams Daily Restaurant and Saloon, Inc., and, after some argument, managed to persuade the proprietor, Mr. Stanley K.

137

Warczinski, Sr., to intrude upon the Honourable Moosenose Bartlett's game of eight-ball and to summon that politico to the telephone.

'Moosenose, this is Wrong Way,' he began.

'This personal or official, Wrong Way?' His Honour replied. 'It had better be official. Interruptions destroy my concentration on my game.'

'Official, Moosenose,' Wrong Way replied.

'In that case, knock off the "Moosenose," ' His Honour said. 'It's Mayor Bartlett to you.'

'Mayor Bartlett,' Wrong Way began. Then he paused. 'Moosenose, you might want to come out here. We got an archbishop about to land.'

'An archbishop?'

'I figured maybe you'd want to know,' Wrong Way said. 'Maybe you could make some Brownie points with Father Cronin.'*

'Good thinking, Wrong Way,' His Honour said. 'I'll be down there just as soon as I can get a police car to run me home for my top hat and mayor's sash. I would consider it a personal favour if you could keep the archbishop on the plane until I get there.'

Wrong Way was then struck with a pang of conscience. He was, after all (though he would have preferred a cleric of Italianate extraction), one of Pastor Sean Cronin's more or less faithful flock. Therefore, he picked up the telephone once again and dialled Father Cronin's parish office.

---

*Father Sean Cronin was pastor and chief Bingo umpire of Christ the King Church. In a moment of passion, His Honour the Mayor had lost his temper and publicly suggested that the Christ the King Church Thursday Bingo games, which he had attended faithfully, perhaps even religiously, for sixteen years, were fixed. He had almost immediately apologized, confessing that he had lost control when, with only a G—48 remaining to be covered on his card in order to win a complete simulated wicker picnic set, he had heard one of the nuns cry, 'Bingo.' The damage had been done, however, and it had come to the mayor's attention that Christ the King's Men's Bingo and Bowling League intended to field a candidate against him in the next mayoralty election.

'Father, this is Wrong Way,' he began.

'Before you start in, Wrong Way,' Father Cronin replied, 'I think you should know that I'm on Mrs. Napolitano's side. What madness possessed a fine broth of a girl like Mary Margaret O'Shaugnessy when she got tied up with a pizza-eater like you is –'

'Father, it's nothing like that,' Wrong Way interrupted.

'What, then?'

'Father, Spruce Harbour is about to be honoured with a visit from an archbishop.'

'You been at the chianti again, Wrong Way? There's been nothing said by the chancellory.'

'Would I lie to you, Father Cronin?'

'Yes, I think you would,' Father Cronin replied. 'I'm trying to deduce your devious purpose in trying to tell me something as preposterous as this. What would an archbishop be doing in Spruce Harbour?'

'Don't say, when the archbishop has come and gone and you didn't see him, that I didn't tell you,' Wrong Way said.

'I'll be right down,' Father Cronin said. 'For your sake, Wrong Way, there had better be an archbishop there when I get there.'

CHAPTER THIRTEEN

'Spruce Harbour,' the pilot called. 'Air Hussid over the outer marker, turning right on final.'

Spruce Harbour International, its dirt runway measuring all of five thousand feet, came into view.

'Full flaps,' the pilot called. 'Stand by to reverse thrust!'

It takes about seven seconds for an idling jet engine to develop full power after the throttles are shoved fully forward. In order to get the DC–9 to stop on Spruce Harbour's main (and only) runway, reverse thrust (in which the engines push backward) was required from the moment the plane touched down, and to get this, it was necessary to start the reverse-thrust process seven seconds before touchdown. This was a tricky manoeuvre requiring the finest depth-and-time judgment.

'Full reverse thrust,' the pilot called. The engineer threw the thrust lever into reverse and then shoved the throttles full forward. The co-pilot, seeing that the archbishop was a little busy at the moment getting the bird on the ground, did what he could to help. He crossed himself and began to move his lips in silent prayer.

In the aisle of the main cabin, Boris Alexandrovich Korsky-Rimsakov (who ignored all signs, including ones reading FASTEN SEAT BELTS, in the belief that they were intended only for people too stupid to figure things out for themselves) stood facing the rear of the aircraft, wondering where everyone, specifically the steward who had been ordered two full minutes ago to deliver a Brandy Alexander, had gone.

The engines roared, and Boris looked indignant. They were making so much noise that even *his* shouting would be hard to hear.

He opened his mouth to shout. At that instant the plane

touched down, reverse thrust came into play no more than half a second after touchdown. The airplane immediately began to slow. Boris Alexandrovich Korsky-Rimsakov's body, obeying certain laws of physics, did not slow down.

'Jesus Christ!' he shouted, as, in a semi-weightless state, he went flying down the aisle. 'Who's driving this bus?'

He came to a stop against the bulkhead that separated the pilot's compartment (or cockpit) from the rest of the plane. It wasn't an irresistible force meeting an immovable object — just three hundred pounds of bone and muscle meeting reinforced aluminium and thin teakwood panelling. The reinforced aluminium gave. The door to the pilot's compartment was immediately twisted and warped and generally put out of commission. Boris' head went through the teakwood veneer the way ladies' fingers go through Brand X plastic wrap in television commercials. He was, so to speak, flying straight and level at the moment of impact, and since his shoulders were eight inches wider than the door frame, this brought his flight to a sudden halt.

The DC–9's landing was witnessed by a number of people, including the pilot of a Beech Bonanza, one V. D. Evans, who was an itinerant peddler of used aviation radios. He had, moments before, landed on the field, which his aviation charts described as 'a sub-marginal facility, suitable for use only in desperation.' He was so fascinated by the sight of the DC–9 making its approach to the field that he forgot he was also piloting a plane and taxied his Bonanza into a rather odd vehicle that had driven onto the field at about the same time.

The vehicle, which consisted of wheels two feet wide and ten feet tall, a large diesel engine, and little else, was a familiar sight in the Louisiana marshes, where such devices, known as swamp buggies, were used for travel through swamps. It was something of an understatement to say that it was *not* the sort of thing Mr. Evans had expected to find on the rock-bound coast of Maine. He got out of the Bonanza, examined his propeller — now twisted into the shape of a pretzel — rubbed his eyes, examined what he had run into, rubbed his eyes again, looked down Spruce Harbour's five-thousand-foot runway — and saw the DC–9 lumbering in his direction. He then did what any experienced pilot would do in such circumstances. He reached into the cockpit, removed the case marked FOR EMERGENCY USE ONLY, and withdrew a quart bottle of Old Highland Dew Scotch Whisky.

He uncapped same and drank deeply. When he put the bottle down, he found himself being examined by two gentlemen who had apparently just descended from the swamp buggy.

'Under the circumstances,' the taller of the two said, 'I think it only fair that you should have a snort of that, Trapper John.'

'Why should this funny-looking fellow get a snort of *my* booze?' Mr. Evans demanded suspiciously.

'I think, if the police should investigate this accident, that you should *both* reek of spiritous liquors,' the taller man said. 'Otherwise, my fine fellow, you're liable to be charged with taxi-ing under the influence.'

'You have a point,' Evans said, after furrowing his brow thoughtfully. He handed the bottle to the gentleman described as Trapper John, who also took a deep draught from its rather shapely neck.

'What is that thing, anyway?' Evans demanded.

'It's a swamp buggy,' the tall man said. 'You mean you couldn't tell?'

'And now, sir, if you will excuse us, Hawkeye and I have to go greet the archbishop,' Trapper John said. He handed him the bottle. 'I expect your insurance company will be hearing from mine.'

Evans watched as they walked to the side of the runway. In a moment, siren screaming, whooper whooping, red-white-and-blue gumball machine flashing, a two-year-old Ford marked SPRUCE HARBOUR POLICE DEPARTMENT came racing up.

The back door opened. A portly, red-faced man jumped

out. With some effort, he wrestled on a purple sash emblazoned with gold letters spelling out MAYOR. When the sash was in place, he reached into the police car and came out with a somewhat dented silk top hat.

'To what do we owe this alleged honour, Moosenose?' Hawkeye asked.

'I came to pay my respects to the archbishop,' His Honour replied.

'I heard about what you said about the Bingo game, Moosenose,' Trapper John said. 'But you're doomed. We Irish hold grudges practically forever.'

Another car raced up, this one a new Buick.* Father Sean Cronin leapt from behind the wheel.

'I must say that I'm more than a bit disappointed to see two fine surgeons – even though you are a back-slider, McIntyre – in the company of the likes of him,' Father Cronin said, by way of greeting. 'Where's the archbishop?'

Hawkeye and Trapper pointed to the DC–9, which was taxiing up to them.

Finally a Ford station wagon came racing up and slid to a halt.

'I do believe that it's the mother of my children,' Hawkeye said.

'I know it is,' Trapper John said. 'I could tell by the way she slid to a stop.'

'Are we too late?' Mary Pierce cried.

The DC–9 stopped. The roar of its engines died to a whine. Wrong Way appeared at the wheel of a somewhat rusty pickup truck that had a flight of stairs mounted on its back end. He backed it up to the airplane. The door opened.

---

*The vehicle had been presented to Father Cronin as a small token of the respect and affection of his flock a week after the Rev. Casper T. Hollowell, pastor of the Prince of Peace Lutheran Church, which was located next to Christ the King, had been presented with a new Oldsmobile 98 as a small token of the respect and affection of *his* flock.

143

A slight gentleman in his fifties appeared. He was attired in black trousers and a flaming yellow nylon zipper jacket. He was standing sideways so that the assembled multitudes could read what had been sewn onto the back of the jacket. Purple felt letters spelled out CAJUN AIR FORCE. A yellow-and-purple baseball cap with gold embroidered scrollwork on the bill sat jauntily atop his head.

As soon as the stairs were in place, he ran down them quickly. As he came closer, what was sewn on the front of the jacket became legible. There were a set of Cajun Air Force wings (wings in which the traditional shield had been replaced by a oil-well drilling rig) on the right breast, and, on the left, the words DAGO RED.

'It seems to me,' Father Cronin sniffed, 'that that airline, whatever it is, could have paid a little more attention to the uniforms of its crew, since His Eminence is aboard.'

'Dago Red!' Hawkeye cried, wrapping his arms around the smaller man, hugging him, lifting him off the ground. Finally he set him down, and Trapper John repeated the process.

'Shame on you, Johnny McIntyre, be glad yer mother couldn't see that shameful demonstration,' Father Cronin said. 'Carousing around like that when, for all you know, His Eminence himself might be looking out the window.'

'Father Cronin —' Hawkeye began.

'I trust,' Father Cronin said, interrupting him and addressing Dago Red, 'that His Eminence had a nice flight?'

'Yes,' Dago Red replied. 'A nice flight.'

'Father Cronin —' Trapper John began, and was also cut off.

'Little fella, would ye be so good as to run back up them steps and tell His Eminence that Father Sean Cronin is here to welcome His Eminence to Spruce Harbour?'

'That'll have to wait,' Dago Red said. 'Boris ran his head through the cockpit wall, Hawkeye. You'd better go have a look.'

'Perhaps ye didn't understand me, little fella,' Father

144

Cronin said. 'Or perhaps ye think I'm wearin' my collar this way because I don't own a necktie. So I'll say it slow, and in words of one syllable. I am Father Sean Cronin, a priest of the church for twenty years, and I'm askin' ye to get back up them steps and tell His Eminence the archbishop that Father Sean Cronin is down here, waitin' to welcome him to fair Spruce Harbour.'

'Me, too,' Mayor Moosenose Bartlett said. 'You can consider the good Father's request, Shorty, as an order from the City of Spruce Harbour as well.'

'Whatever happened to separation of church and state?' Hawkeye asked as he started to trot up the flight of steps.

'May I say something?' Trapper John inquired.

'Dago Red!' Mary Pierce cried, running up to the little man and putting her arms around him. 'I'm so glad to see you. I thought Hawkeye was making the whole thing up.'

'How are you, Mary?' Dago Red said. He looked at Lucinda McIntyre. 'And Lucinda McIntyre! I didn't recognize you, my dear, in a dress.'

Lucinda McIntyre kissed Dago Red on the forehead. Lucinda was given to using large amounts of Blazing Passion Purple Lip Rouge to enhance what she (but practically no one else) thought of as her sexless lips. The result of this was that Dago Red emerged from the embrace with the clear imprint of female lips on his forehead. This was obvious to everyone, including Father Cronin.

'Little fella,' he said, 'be good enough to conceal the marks of your shameless carryin' on from the eyes of the good archbishop.'

'Trapper,' Hawkeye called from the top of the stairs, 'I'm afraid he'll live, but we'll need a hacksaw to cut him free from the door.'

A voice was suddenly heard. It was a voice that had thrilled millions and had caused its owner to be declared a National Treasure of the Republic of France. It caused a tremor to move through the crowd here now – not because of its interpretation of, say, the musical genius of Verdi,

145

Bellini, or Bizet, but because its owner, who had total recall, was recalling all the words* he had learned in the 223rd Infantry.

'What the ( ) has happened? Why the ( ) am I stuck in this ( )ing door? Why the ( ) isn't someone doing some ( )ing thing to get me out of this ( )ing door? Hawkeye! You ( )ing chancre mechanic, can't you see that I'm bleeding grievously from this wound on my ( )ing nose?'

'Oh, my goodness!' Father Cronin said. 'And with the archbishop on board, where he can hear everything!'

'The archbishop's not on board,' Dago Red said.

'He's *not*?' Father Cronin said.

'Wrong Way, I knew you couldn't be trusted,' Mayor Moosenose Bartlett said.

'Ye can't trust any of them pizza-eaters,' Father Cronin said. 'They're as crooked as politicians.'

'That's a terrible thing to say!' Dago Red said. 'Shame on you, Father!'

'I can't believe my ears!' Father Cronin said. 'Lay people don't go around sayin' things like that to priests of the Church! It works the other way around. Shame on *you*, you little heathen! I knew the minute I laid my eyes on you that you were some kind of a Protestant troublemaker!'

The Very Reverend Monsignor Pancho de Malaga y de Villa, wearing one of those ankle-length black garments and round-crowned, round-brimmed hats that have, for the last couple of centuries, been considered the height of ecclesiastical fashion for monsignori around Vatican City, appeared at the door of the aircraft.

'Excuse me, Your Eminence,' he called. 'Mr. Korsky-Rimsakov asks that you hold his hand while they cut him free from the door.'

*The words Mr. Korsky-Rimsakov used in his pain and anguish cannot, of course, be printed in a morally uplifting tome such as this one. Those whose limited imaginations will not permit them to fill in the appropriate blank spaces should get in touch with a former U.S. Army infantryman, or, in a pinch, a Marine.

'Coming!' Dago Red called, and he bounded back up the stairs.

Father Cronin turned to Mary Pierce. While she wasn't one of his faithful flock, Father Cronin felt that someone named Mary should have secret religious leanings, and further that someone sharing the life of Dr. Hawkeye Pierce was a likely candidate for sainthood via a lifetime of martyrdom.

'Mary, my girl,' he said, 'my old ears must be failing me. Did you happen to catch what that fine-looking monsignor called that little heathen?'

'What little heathen?' Mary Pierce asked.

'The little Protestant one in the yellow-and-purple nylon jacket, that one,' Father Cronin clarified.

'Oh, Father Cronin, Archbishop Mulcahy's not a heathen,' Lucinda McIntyre said. 'He's an Eminence.'

'Then what's he dressed up like that for? Whoever heard of an archbishop running around in a yellow-and-purple jacket with "Dago Red" sewed on it?'

'Why don't you ask him?' Moosenose Bartlett suggested.

'I'm sure His Eminence has his reasons, and very good ones,' Father Cronin said firmly. 'Although, at the moment, I can't imagine what they might be.'

They all stood at the foot of the stairs, looking up at the door to the airplane, from which came the sounds of a hacksaw working its way through aluminium. These sounds were punctuated by loud groans. Finally, Monsignor Pancho de Malaga y de Villa appeared in the door and descended the stairs.

'Mary, Lucinda,' he said to Mesdames Pierce and McIntyre, 'I'm so glad you're here. The archbishop was hoping you would be.'

'Anything Dago Red wants, Pancho,' Mary Pierce said. 'You know that.'

'Monsignor,' Father Cronin said. 'I'm Father Sean Cronin, and I'm a friend of these fine ladies, even though one of them is a Protestant.'

147

'He thought Dago Red was a heathen,' Lucinda McIntyre offered helpfully. 'Isn't that the funniest thing you ever heard?'

'Not quite,' the monsignor said, giving Father Cronin a somewhat frosty glance.

'What happened to Old Bull Bellow?'

'He was standing in the aisle when His Eminence put the bird into full reverse thrust,' replied the monsignor, who had picked up some aviation lingo. 'And he kept flying, so to speak.'

'But he's going to be all right?' Lucinda asked.

'Oh, yes,' the monsignor said.

'Pity,' Mary Pierce said.

'You say Dago Red wanted to see us?' Lucinda asked.

'We have a small problem,' the monsignor said. 'His Eminence hoped that you would be willing to help.'

'As Mary said,' Lucinda replied. 'Anything Dago Red wants, Dago Red gets.'

'I felt sure you'd feel that way,' the monsignor said.

'What can we do?' Mary Pierce asked.

'I think His Eminence would rather ask you himself,' the monsignor said. He looked up at the airplane. 'And here he comes.'

'Speak of the devil,' Lucinda McIntyre said.

His Eminence the Archbishop of Swengchan came down the stairs.

'Boris'll be all right,' he said.

'Pity,' Mary Pierce replied. 'I was hoping he'd broken his neck or something.'

'Mary, Lucinda,' His Eminence said. 'I need a favour from you.'

'As my good friend Mary was just saying, Dago Red,' Father Cronin said. 'Anything you want!'

'Now see here, you,' His Eminence said, suddenly flaring. 'I'll stand here and take being called a heathen by you, because you're obviously not too bright, but only my friends get to call me "Dago Red." You got that?'

148

'Yes, of course, Your Eminence,' Father Cronin said.

Boris Alexandrovich Korsky-Rimsakov at that moment appeared at the door of the airplane. He was wearing a sky-blue silk dressing gown with an ermine collar, a Russian-style fur cap, and a Band-Aid on his nose. His right hand held a pint-sized brandy sniffer, recently nearly filled from a half-gallon jug of Courvoisier, which he held in his left hand.

'Dry your tears, Mary and Lucinda,' he cried. 'God had heard your prayers – or at least decided on His own that my incomparable voice should not be stilled – and I will live!'

'Whoopee!' Mary Pierce said.

'Where's your luggage?' Boris asked.

'We're not going anywhere,' Lucinda McIntyre said. 'That's how come no luggage.'

'You're sure?'

'Absolutely positive,' Mary Pierce said. 'Absolutely.'

'Pity,' Boris said. 'Miami, I am told, is rather nice, compared to here, this time of year.'

'We're not going to Miami,' Lucinda McIntyre said. 'And neither are Trapper John . . .'

'Or Hawkeye,' Mary said to complete the non-negotiable statement of fact.

Another bearded man, almost as large as Boris, appeared beside him at the head of the stairway. He shrank from the light, putting his hands over his eyes. Then he jabbed Boris in the arm. Without looking at him, Boris handed him the half-gallon jug of Courvoisier cognac. The bearded man took a large pull at the neck, handed the bottle back, and peered curiously around him.

'Jesus Christ!' he said. 'Where in hell we are? Who dat funny-looking fella in the funny hat?'

'Moosenose,' Mary Pierce said. 'Say hello to François Mulligan.'

'On behalf of the City Administration and the Chamber of Commerce of Beautiful Spruce Harbour on the Bay,' Moosenose said sonorously, 'sometimes referred to as the

149

Pearl of Maine, welcome. Welcome to our fair city, Mr. Mulligan.'

'Jesus, he sure talk funny, don't he, Boris?' Mulligan said, wrapping an arm around Boris' shoulders as they descended the stairs. The stairs mounted on the back of Wrong Way's pickup truck creaked ominously under the burden, but the journey was completed safely.

François took the Courvoisier bottle from Boris, carefully wiped its neck on his shirttail, and extended it to Moosenose.

'Don't mind if I do,' Moosenose replied.

'Hello dere, pretty Madame Pierce,' François said, finally focusing his eyes on her. 'You and Madame McIntyre goin' to Miami wit us, huh?'

'I think not, François,' Mary Pierce said. 'Thank you just the same.'

'You ought to come along,' François pursued. 'We're going to have a little party.'

'That thought occurred to us, François,' Lucinda said. 'We'll just have to make that sacrifice.'

'And so will Hawkeye,' Mary began.

'And Trapper John,' Lucinda finished.

'Mary, Lucinda!' said Dago Red. 'About that little favour?'

'What about it?'

'May I speak to you privately?' Dago Red asked, taking a lady's arm in each hand and leading them under the wing and behind the landing gear, where they were concealed from sight and could converse privately.

'Far be it from me, Dago Red, to be even a teensy-weensy bit suspicious of an archbishop, but what, exactly, do you have in mind, favour-wise?' Mary Pierce asked.

'You heard François say that he was going to Miami?'

'Indeed I did,' Mary replied. 'That's why Hawkeye's *not* going.'

'And you gathered, I suppose, that Boris is also going to be there?'

150

'That's why my Trapper's going to stay home,' Lucinda replied. 'His carcass by the hearth.'

'I wouldn't be at all surprised if His Royal Highness Whatsisname was also going to Miami,' Mary said.

'You are very perceptive, Mary,' Dago Red said. 'Hassan is on the plane.'

'That, to coin a phrase, puts the cork in the jug,' Mary Pierce said. 'I'm just surprised, Dago Red, that you're going too. What if your boss should hear about it?'

'But you don't know *why* we're all going,' Dago Red said.

'Let me make a wild guess,' Mary said. 'Horsey and Hot Lips are going to fly over from New Orleans.'

'Just Hot Lips. Horsey's on the plane too. We went to Alaska to get him.'

'On purpose, you mean? Or was he going to be lynched by the Eskimos, and you saw it as your misguided Christian duty to save his skin?'

The archbishop didn't reply directly to the question.

'Mary,' he said. 'Let me put it to you this way. Could you ... and Lucinda, too, of course ... really be so cold, cruel, and callous as to let a man of my age, in the twilight of his years on earth, go to Miami alone with Boris, François, and Horsey?'

'You can stay here while they go to Miami,' Mary replied.

'Oh, but I can't. I have to go and explain Hot Lips' holy relic to the family Gomez y Sanchez.' He paused. 'What I mean to say is that I will explain that there are holy relics and then there are *holy relics*.'

'Go over that again,' Mary said. 'I'd have sworn you said, "Hot Lips' holy relic." '

He did.

Three minutes later, Mesdames Pierce and McIntyre marched up the stairs mounted on the back of Wrong Way Napolitano's pickup truck and into the interior of Air Hussid DC–9 Number Twelve behind His Eminence the Archbishop of Swengchan.

Shielding their eyes as they marched past the door to the

Royal Cabin, they proceeded to the forward compartment, where Dr. and Mrs. Walter Waldowski and Wanda were having a bite to eat.

'Oh, Your Eminence!' Mrs. Waldowski said. 'What an unexpected pleasure!'

'Although you ladies have exchanged Christmas cards,' Dago Red said, 'I don't believe you've met. Mary Pierce, Lucinda McIntyre, this is Wilma Waldowski.'

'Oh, how nice!' Wilma Waldowski said.

'Get your bags, dear,' Mary Pierce said. 'You're getting off!'

'I beg your pardon?'

'We'll explain later,' Lucinda McIntyre said.

'I beg your pardon?'

'Trust me, Wilma,' Dago Red said. 'It's better this way.'

'I don't quite understand,' Wilma Waldowski said.

'Remember saying "for better or for worse"?' Mary Pierce said. 'Well, dear, that wasn't in the ceremony for nothing.'

'You heard the archbishop, Walter,' Wilma said to her husband. 'Get up, put that Bloody Mary down, and get our bags.'

'Walter's not going,' Dago Red said. 'Or, more precisely, Walter's not getting off. I mean, he's going, and you're not.'

'What's he going to do?' Wilma demanded.

'I don't think, dear,' Mary Pierce said, 'that you really want to know.'

'Boston Area Control,' the pilot said. 'Air Hussid Twelve on the ground at Spruce Harbour International requests route and altitude for Direct Miami.'

'Air Hussid Twelve, Boston, say again your location?'

'Air Hussid Twelve on the ground at Spruce Harbour International.'

'Air Hussid Twelve, what is your type of aircraft?'

'Boston, Air Hussid Twelve is a DC–9 F aircraft.'

'Boston advises Air Hussid that Spruce Harbour International is a five-thousand-foot dirt runway and will not take an aircraft the size of a DC–9.'

'Boston,' the pilot responded, just a trifle smugly, 'that would depend on just who is flying the DC–9. I say again, request route and altitude for Direct Miami.'

'Oh, what the hell,' Boston responded. 'Boston Area Control clears Air Hussid Twelve for takeoff from Spruce Harbour. Climb to flight level three zero thousand, take Victor Twelve, and report over Boston.'

'Roger, Boston. Air Hussid understands Victor Twelve at three zero thousand.' The pilot looked out the cockpit window, made the sign of blessing to Father Sean Cronin and the Honourable Moosenose Bartlett (who stood respectfully by the side of the runway), and then shoved the throttles forward. 'Air Hussid rolling,' he said into his microphone.

'Let that be a lesson to ye, Moosenose Bartlett,' Father Cronin said as the plane raced down the runway. 'A church that can send its archbishop soaring off into the wild blue yonder at the controls of a great jet aircraft like that one doesn't need to be fixing its Bingo games.'

CHAPTER FOURTEEN

Senator J. Ellwood ('Jaws') Fisch (Radical-Liberal, Calif.) was not really as stupid as his many critics wanted people to believe. He could indeed, despite slanderous suggestions to the contrary, read without moving his lips and walk and chew gum at the same time. He proved this, time and time again, to the enthusiastic applause of his many fans (most of whom were registered lobbyists), at cocktail parties from one end of the District of Columbia to the other.

Objective viewers – of which, it is true, there were very few – found that the senator was actually setting a standard the government might well emulate. That is to say, he was doing a great deal with very little.

He had come to the Senate with only one solid talent, an uncanny (if well-rehearsed) ability to talk like the late President John F. Kennedy. On the other end of the scale was the senator's unfortunate predilection for nibbling playfully on the lower limbs of his female companions. The affectionate appellation 'Jaws' by which he was known did *not* actually make reference to his well-polished, somewhat outsized teeth, although the senator's assistant for policy research, who handled his public relations, P. Kenyon Quirtman (GS-18, $36,990 per annum), spent at least half his time buttressing that popular misconception.

The senator actually possessed an ability that few of his fellows in what has been laughingly called 'The World's Most Exclusive Club' possessed. He recognized his own limitations. Whatever else could (and usually was) said about him, Senator Jaws Fisch did not believe that God had selected him to save the country from the foolish ambitions of its citizens. Shortly after being sworn in, he had confessed to the president pro tempore of the Senate that he knew absolutely nothing about finance, international relations,

154

ecology, law, or Indian affairs, and that his knowledge of military affairs was limited to his six-month period of service as a PFC in the Quartermaster Corps.

'We have just the spot for you, Senator,' the president pro tempore had said. 'Just the place for someone of your talents.'

Senator Fisch had been assigned, as eleventh ranking member, to the eleven-man Senate Subcommittee on Minorities. He understood, of course, that the important minorities – the Afro-Americans, the Irish Americans, the Jewish Americans, the Polish Americans, the Italian Americans, the Latin Americans, and the American Americans (or 'Indians') naturally were assigned to the more important senators. He was perfectly happy with what he got – the French Americans.

The French Americans, by and large, didn't require much of his time. For one thing, there weren't very many of them, and they so far had shown no insatiable hunger to burn the American flag on the steps of our nation's Capitol to call attention to their plight.

Fisch's position carried with it certain perquisites. For one thing, he got to go to Paris a lot. And he went free, for Air France had presented him with a pass as a small token of its gratitude for all that he was doing for the oppressed French Americans in what, for some reason the senator didn't quite understand, they insisted on calling 'Les États Unis.'

Soon after arriving for the first time in France, Fisch had met the most *charming* French diplomat, who had introduced him to a procession of attractive young women, all of whom confessed that their idea of heaven on earth was to be nibbled on the thigh by a handsome and talented U.S. senator. These hadn't been run-of-the-mill French floozies, either. Each and every one had been well educated, and in their company, he had acquired in addition to other things, quite a bit of knowledge about that magnificent French droop-nosed supersonic aircraft, Le Discorde, and the whole

155

new world of aviation wonders that would open up the minute it was granted U.S. landing rights. . . .

Senator Fisch was quite surprised and more than a little worried when the chairman of the Subcommittee on Minorities, the Honourable Christopher Columbus ('C. C.') Cacciatore (Ethnic-Democrat, N.J.), sent word to him, via an underling, that he wanted to see him. So far as Senator Fisch knew, he had been doing a good job. His record was perfect: everything that Senator C. C. Cacciatore had voted for *he* had voted for, and everything that the New Jersey senator had voted against Senator Jaws Fisch had also voted against.

The Subcommittee on Minorities did not, of course, occupy all of Senator Cacciatore's time and talents. The senator was chairman of the Senate Committee on Internal Operations. It was he who assigned office space, secretarial help, and, most important, it was his eagle eye that went over senatorial expense accounts.

Senators who defied Senator Cacciatore did so at their own peril. Those who were foolhardy enough to vote against some bill Senator Cacciatore favoured soon found themselves installed in basement offices in, say, the Bethesda, Maryland, annex of the Smithsonian Institution and answering constituents' mail on Sears, Roebuck portable typewriters, rather than conducting the nation's business from one of the Senate office buildings with the best office equipment the taxpayers' money could buy.

One of the Senate's most cherished legends featured the foolhardy senator (most people felt he must have been drinking at the time) who had voted against Senator Cacciatore *three times in a row*. Senator Cacciatore had risen to that challenge with imagination and determination. The renegade senator's mail had been returned to his constituents stamped NOT KNOWN AT THIS ADDRESS; the one telephone that was installed in his office in the Bureau of Indian Affairs was the kind that hung on the wall and required a dime to get it going; and, to put the cherry on the cake, when the senator had invoked the sacred senatorial

156

privilege and arranged to catch a ride home on an Air Force plane, he'd 'happened' to be seated on the last piston-engine transport aircraft in active service – which had 'happened' to get itself re-routed after takeoff for a trip to Brisbane, Australia, via Buenos Aires, Capetown, and New Delhi.

Although his conscience was clear, Senator Jaws Fisch nevertheless prepared for his audience with Senator Cacciatore with great care. He stopped by the Capitol Liquor Store and picked up a case of the very best chianti. He dressed with care in his best Italian silk suit and Gucci loafers, and he doused himself liberally with an eau de cologne known as 'Flora del Napoli.'

When he was finally ushered into the senator's presence, he carried, conspicuously, a copy of *Michelangelo, The World's Greatest Genius* under his arm. P. Kenyon Quirtman, his senior assistant for policy research, preceded him, carrying the case of chianti on his shoulders.

'*Buono giorno, Don* Christopher,' Senator Fisch said.

'Close your mouth, your teeth blind me,' the senator replied. He stood by patiently as Mr. Quirtman reverently opened the case of chianti and presented him with a raffia-wrapped bottle. The senator examined the bottle carefully.

'You're a good boy, Fisch,' Senator Cacciatore said. 'Not too bright, but you mean well. Next time, tell the man who the vino is for, and he'll get you the good stuff.'

'Make a note of that, Quirtman,' Senator Fisch replied. 'Nothing is too good for our beloved Senator Cacciatore.'

'That's the idea,' the senator replied. 'Keep that in mind.' He turned to Mr. Quirtman and dismissed him with a wave of his hand. Mr. Quirtman backed out of the room.

'So tell me, Jaws, how's things?'

'Just fine, Senator, thank you kindly.'

'So where's your manners? You're not going to ask how's things by *me*?'

'Of course I am,' Senator Fisch said. 'I just didn't want to seem forward, Senator.'

'So ask.'

'How are things with you, Senator Cacciatore?'

'Strange that you should ask, Fisch,' Senator Cacciatore said. 'The truth of the matter is, I got a delicate little problem.'

'I'm sorry, truly sorry, to hear that.'

'That's all you got to say? I tell you I got a delicate little problem, and all you got to say is that you're sorry to hear about it? Maybe I misjudged you. Maybe you'd like to move your office to the Bureau of Indian Affairs.'

'Is there anything I can do, Senator, to help?' Senator Fisch asked.

'Strange that you should ask,' Senator Cacciatore said. 'As it happens, I need a small favour.'

'Name it,' Senator Fisch replied instantly.

'Let me give you a word of advice, Fisch,' Senator Cacciatore said. 'The distilled essence of my long years of public service.'

'Yes, sir?' Senator Fisch asked, sitting up on the edge of his chair.

'Never trust a Cuban,' Senator Cacciatore said.

Senator Fisch took a notepad from the breast pocket of his Italian silk suit, and, moving his lips just a little, wrote those words down. 'Never trust a Cuban,' he said, and looked at Senator Cacciatore again. 'I'll remember that, Senator Cacciatore. I'm grateful to you for sharing your wisdom with me.'

'I told you before, Fisch, don't smile at me. Your teeth blind me.'

'Sorry, Senator,' Fisch said.

'Enough of this beating around the bush,' Senator Cacciatore said. 'Let's get to the heart of the matter. You tell me, Fisch – who was it who went personally to Miami to welcome a boat-load of Cuban refugees?'

'Let me think a moment,' Fisch replied. 'It's right on the tip of my tongue.'

'It was Christopher Columbus Cacciatore, that's who it was!' the senator said.

158

'Of course! How stupid of me!'

'You said it, Fisch, not me,' the senator said. 'And who was it got up on the floor of the Senate and made one of the most brilliant, touching, stirring, and very interesting speeches about how welcoming Cuban refugees to our shores was in the finest tradition of the nation?'

'*That*,' Senator Fisch cried triumphantly, 'I know. Senator Barry Gold –'

'Christopher Columbus Cacciatore, that's who!' Christopher Columbus Cacciatore said.

'Of course.'

'And going back to the very beginning, Fisch – who discovered Cuba?'

'Vasco de Gama?'

'*Mama mia*, you're really dumb, Fisch, you know that?'

'If you say so, Senator,' Senator Fisch replied.

'Christopher *Columbus* discovered Cuba, that's who discovered Cuba!' Senator Cacciatore said. 'The great navigator.'

Scribbling furiously, Senator Fisch wrote 'Christopher Columbus discovered Cuba' on his note pad.

'So we welcome these miserable refugees to our fair shores,' Senator Cacciatore said. 'They come here with nothing but the clothing on their backs. Most of them can't even speak English, for God's sake. All they got, we gave them. Jobs, for example. Out of the goodness of our hearts, Fisch, and closing our eyes to the fact that most of them can't even speak English, we gave them jobs – washing dishes, sweeping floors, digging ditches. Things like that.'

'That's true, Senator,' Senator Fisch agreed.

'Certainly it's true! I said it. We told them this was the land of opportunity, the great melting pot, that success is open to everybody willing to work and sacrifice for it.'

'Right,' Senator Fisch said. 'We did that.'

'Not we, Fisch. Me. I gave that speech. It was one of my better ones.'

'Of course.'

'And how did they repay our generosity?'

'I don't know, sir,' Senator Fisch said.

'They foreclosed on the Friendly Sons of Italy, that's how!' the senator said, his outrage evident in his flushed face.

'I beg your pardon?'

'Why, what did you do, Fisch, burp?'

'I don't quite follow you, Senator,' Senator Fisch said.

'Well, if you were listening to me instead of burping all over, maybe you would have *heard* what I said. Pay attention this time. What I said was that those lousy Cubans *foreclosed* on the Friendly Sons of Italy.'

'They did that, did they?' Senator Fisch replied. 'That certainly was beastly of them, wasn't it?'

'You can say that again, Senator,' C. C. Cacciatore said.

'That certainly was beastly of them, wasn't it?'

'You said it. Right out on the street,' the senator said. 'When Pasquale d'Allesandro called me to tell me about it, he had to call from the gas station on the corner. And while he was making the call, some nefarious scoundrel made off with the Senator Cacciatore Memorial Oil Portrait of Christopher Columbus. They found it later. Some kids ... obviously Cuban kids ... had been using it for a bow-and-arrow target.'

'A portrait of Christopher Columbus? A sacrilege!'

'An *oil* portrait, painted by hand by my wife's cousin's nephew Gino,' the senator said. 'I gave it to the Friendly Sons when they made me an honourable member.'

'That was certainly a generous gesture of you, Senator,' Senator Fisch said.

'Not only was it generous,' the senator replied, 'it got the rotten painting out of the house. My wife's cousin's nephew Gino isn't worth a *pastafazool* as a painter, you should excuse the expression.'

'Certainly,' Senator Fisch said. 'But, Senator, I'm a little confused about how the Cubans connect with all this.'

'You're not very bright, Fisch, as I already told you. *Twice*, I told you. They foreclosed on the Friendly Sons of Italy. That's what they have to do with it!'

160

'How did they do that?'

'They sent the Dade County sheriff down to the Friendly Sons of Italy hall with a foreclosure notice. He threw the furniture, not to mention sixteen Friendly Sons, right out onto the street. Just because they were a little late with the mortgage payment.'

'How late?'

'What's twelve, fifteen months? A fleeting instant in the history of the universe, that's what it is. The Friendly Sons of Italy were a fleeting instant, no more, late with their mortgage payment, and those lousy Cubans had them foreclosed and evicted! That's gratitude for you! Never trust a Cuban, Fisch – remember that!'

'I will, Senator, I will,' Fisch replied. 'So the sheriff hired some Cubans to throw the Friendly Sons' furniture out in the street. Outrageous! Beastly! They should have refused, of course.'

'You got it backwards, stupid,' Senator Cacciatore said. 'The *Cubans* hired the *sheriff* to throw the Friendly Sons of Italy and their furniture out onto the street. He gets seventy-five bucks for an eviction, and a hundred and a quarter if he has to throw the furniture out too.'

'I see. And just where do the Cubans come in?'

'You wouldn't believe it!'

'I guess I wouldn't believe it if you told me,' Senator Fisch agreed.

'Guess who held the mortgage?'

'I give up.'

'The Great Melting Pot Savings & Loan, that's who,' Senator Cacciatore said. 'What do you think about that?'

'It's a catchy name, I'll say that,' Senator Fisch replied.

'So when Pasquale d'Allesandro called me up and told me the Friendly Sons had been evicted, I of course took appropriate action.'

'Which was?'

'I called the Great Melting Pot Savings & Loan in Miami,' the senator said. 'And you know what they told me?' he asked rhetorically. 'They told *me*, Christopher Columbus Cacciatore himself, to go soak my head in a plate of linguini! They said that the Friendly Sons were nothing but a noisy bunch of deadbeats, and that one of the reasons they'd been evicted was because they were trying to clean up the neighbourhood. Can you beat that?'

'That's awful, Senator,' Senator Fisch said.

'I didn't take it lying down, of course,' Senator Cacciatore went on. 'I got right on the phone and called my longtime, close, dear, and personal friend ... Whatsisname? That bald-headed Irisher? The one who always smells of bourbon? He's chairman of the Senate Committee on Savings and Loans. And he told me he'd look into it for me. Said he wanted to go to Miami anyway.'

'And, he, I gather, brought the situation into proper perspective, lent the confronting parties the benefit of his wisdom, and effected a compromise satisfying all?'

'You wouldn't believe what they did to him!' Senator Cacciatore said. 'Not in a million years. It's sacrilege!'

'I suppose I wouldn't believe what they did to him,' Senator Fisch agreed.

'The senator flew down there, of course, just as fast as the Air Force could get him there on a training flight,' Senator Cacciatore said. 'And he put up, as he has put up since it was built, at the Winter Palace ... you know the place, right down the street from the Fountainbleau?'

'I know the place,' Senator Fisch said. 'A splendid hostelry for those of us in government who desperately need a brief respite from the heavy burden of our many duties.'

'Shows how much you know!' Senator Cacciatore snorted. 'But I don't want to egress —'

'I believe you mean to say "digress." '

'Don't you tell me what I mean to say!' Senator Cacciatore snapped. 'I got a lot of seniority on you, Teeth, I mean Fisch, and don't you forget it!'

'No, sir.'

'As I was saying. So ... Whatsisname. You know, with

162

the purple nose ... the distinguished chairman of the Committee on Savings and Loans. Well, just as soon as he'd had a bite to eat, and a swim, and a massage, and a sun bath, he got right down to business. He got in the hotel's limousine and went over to the Great Melting Pot Savings & Loan.'

'Well, I guess that put them in their place?'

'There wasn't anybody that could speak English! What do you think about that?'

'Astounding!'

'So he called a cop, and the cop translated. Do you know that most of the cops in Miami speak Cuban? I wonder what the C.I.A. thinks about that! Right under our noses, our own cops speaking some foreign language.'

'Shocking.'

'So the cop finds out that the Great Melting Pot Savings & Loan is owned by the Land of Opportunity Bank & Trust Company.'

'That certainly sounds subversive,' Senator Fisch, who had caught the drift of things, said.

'The way these lousy Cubans pervert the true meaning of things has to be experienced to be believed,' Senator Cacciatore said. 'Well, they don't call Whatsisname "Old Horse Teeth" for nothing. He wasn't about to give up. So he got back in the limousine and went to the Land of Opportunity Bank & Trust Company. Great big building, forty stories high, overlooking Biscayne Bay. And guess what he found there?'

'More Cubans?'

'You're not as dumb as you look, sometimes, Fisch. Right you are. Whatsisname found out that the Land of Opportunity Bank & Trust Company is a *wholly-owned subsidiary* of something called Cuba Libre Enterprises, Inc. Can you imagine anything more disrespectful toward our national image than naming a company after some *drink*?'

'Shocking!'

'Well, Whatsisname found out who owned Cuba Libre

Enterprises, Inc. They were hiding out in the penthouse of . . . you won't believe this, Fisch.'

'I guess I won't believe it,' Fisch said.

'The Winter Palace. Right up on top! Sitting up there, sucking on those stinking cigars, and looking down at all the decent folk of Miami Beach.'

'Outrageous!'

'Well, he went and spoke with them. He told them that, speaking as a U.S. senator, he felt that it was a pretty rotten thing for a bunch of lousy immigrants to foreclose a mortgage on a fine, patriotic, native group of one-hundred-per cent Americans like the Friendly Sons of Italy.'

'And what did they say?'

'The mob . . . they call it the family, can you imagine that? . . . is run by some old lady named Doña Antoinetta. You won't believe what she did.'

'Try me, Senator.'

'She said she hadn't liked purple-nosed Irishmen when she lived in Cuba, and nothing that had happened to her since she'd come to the United States had made her change her mind.'

'No!'

'Don't interrupt, it gets worse. Guess what happened when he got back to his room?'

'I can't imagine.'

'The manager of the Winter Palace . . . a Cuban, of course . . . came knocking at the door. He had a bellboy with him and the house detective. The bellboy grabbed the complimentary bowl of fruit off the coffee table. The house detective went around counting glasses and towels and the stationery in the desk drawers. Then the manager said that they were sorry, but they needed the room, and Whatsisname would have to make other arrangements. He had thirty minutes to get out of the room.'

'I've never heard of a worse insult to a United States senator!'

'*I* have. Can you believe that the manager handed

164

Whatsisname a *bill*? I mean, he actually expected a United States *senator*, Fisch, one of *us*, to pay not only for his hotel room and his food, but also for the swim in the pool, the extra towel, his suntan lotion, and, rubbing salt into the wound, even the use of the hotel limousine!'

'Senators never pay for that stuff,' Fisch said. 'It's what they call a fringe benefit. I mean, why give your life to serving the public if you can't expect a little fringe benefit or two?'

'Precisely, my boy,' Senator Cacciatore said. 'My thinking exactly.'

'Whatsisname isn't going to take that insult to the dignity of the United States Senate lying down, is he?'

'Of course not, Fisch, and that's where you come in.'

'*I* come in? What can I do?'

'Senator,' Senator Cacciatore said, putting down his glass of chianti and drawing himself up to his full five feet, six and three-quarter inches, 'duty calls! You are now chairman of the United States Senate Subcommittee on F.B.I. and other Investigative Body Relations!'

'Senator,' Senator Fisch said, teeth flashing, cheeks flushing, boyish haircut wagging like a Scottie's tail, 'I'm truly and deeply honoured. You have my assurance that I will leave no stone upturned, no —'

'That's stone *un*turned, Fisch,' Senator Cacciatore corrected him. '*Un*turned. That means you're supposed to turn them over. What you said —'

'Senator, what is the real meaning of my appointment?' Senator Fisch said. 'Just between us U.S. senators, not for publication or attribution?'

'It means that Whatsisname and I got together and talked this over, and decided the best way to get those lousy, ungrateful Cubans is to sic the F.B.I. on them.'

'Good thinking!'

'We thought about the I.R.S. of course,' Senator Cacciatore said, 'but we decided, let sleeping dogs lie. "The further one can stay from the I.R.S.," as I always say.

Whatever you can say about the F.B.I., they don't ask embarrassing questions about deductions.'

'But what do *I* have to do with this, Senator?'

'Just as soon as the Air Force can fly your teeth, I mean your tail, there, Fisch, you go to Miami and get in touch with the F.B.I. agent in charge. His name is Birch Beebe. He'll tell you whatever he finds out, and you'll tell me.'

'Why can't he just get on the phone and tell you himself?'

'Because *I* want him to tell *you*, Senator,' Senator Cacciatore said. 'How would it look if it got out that I, Senator Christopher Columbus Cacciatore, beloved chairman of the Senate Committee on Internal Operations and dean of the Congressional Italian-American Caucus, was using the F.B.I. to settle a personal grudge?'

'People wouldn't think you capable of behaviour as despicable as that, Senator,' Fisch said loyally.

'But you and I, Fisch,' Senator Cacciatore said, laughing a little laugh that made Senator Fisch's waving boyish locks freeze in place, 'know better, don't we?'

CHAPTER FIFTEEN

His Excellency, Patrick Michael O'Grogarty, Bishop of the Diocese of Greater Miami and the Florida Keys, would have much preferred to put off a requested pastoral call upon Doña Antoinetta, matriarch of the family Gomez y Sanchez, for at least a couple of days. He needed a couple of days to recuperate from the living nightmare he had gone through in Paris. But, on the other hand, the bishop had known that becoming a bishop would mean making certain sacrifices, and this was apparently one of those times when he had to make one.

The family Gomez y Sanchez were not only devout members of his flock, but generously devout members of his flock, which was more than the bishop could say for some people he knew. Considering the wide variety of good works to which the family Gomez y Sanchez contributed very generously, it seemed to the bishop that going to see Doña Antoinetta at her request was his duty.

Even if the pastoral visit required that he hear her confession. Oh, how tired he was of that confession!

Looking just a little wan and peaked, the bishop walked out the front door of his chancellory and stepped to the kerb. The familiar black limousine was waiting for him, its chauffeur holding the door open for him.

Ten minutes later, it pulled up beneath the gilted concrete marquee of the Winter Palace. The brothers Gomez y Sanchez, plus the general manager of the hotel, the bell captain, and the doorman (the latter attired in a faithful reproduction of the uniform of a lieutenant general of the Czarist household cavalry) awaited him.

The doorman pulled the door open and snapped to a salute.

'Welcome to the Winter Palace, Your Holiness,' he said.

'I'm just a simple bishop,' the bishop said. 'I've told you that before.'

The bell captain snatched, not without difficulty, the bishop's attaché case out of his hands. The general manager of the Winter Palace bowed.

'So nice to see you, Your Excellency,' Salvador Gomez y Sanchez said.

'You're looking good, Your Excellency,' Carlos Gomez y Sanchez said.

'Doña Antoinetta will be so pleased,' Juan Gomez y Sanchez said. 'Right this way, please!'

As the bishop permitted himself to be led inside the Winter Palace, he glanced behind him. A black Chevrolet sedan bearing four different radio antennae and carrying two bearded men had pulled in behind his limousine. He thought he'd noticed the car outside the chancellory, but the men in that car, he remembered, had been un-bearded – i.e., smooth shaven. He thought he must be mistaken. *He* knew how much of a strain he'd been under lately.

But he glanced behind him again as he was ushered through the swinging plate glass door marked HOT.*

One of the bearded men was getting out of the black Chevrolet. He was carrying a tool box and wearing a zippered jacket with AJAX TV REPAIR COMPANY lettered on it. But the bishop got only a glimpse of the workman, for the brothers Gomez y Sanchez were hustling him along.

Red velvet-covered ropes suspended from brass floor stands had been erected along the path from the door to one of the elevators, presumably to keep the bishop separated

---

*In keeping with the Russian decor of the establishment, legends corresponding to 'In' and 'Out' on the glass doors were lettered in gold, Cyrillic-alphabet letters. The previous owners had not and the present owners did not read Russian, nor had the sign painter had such knowledge. The bishop spoke Russian, but did not feel it his place to point out that what the Cyrillic lettering actually spelled out was 'Hot' and 'Cold,' rather than, as popular belief had it, 'In' and 'Out.'

from the guests. The chief elevator operator himself stood at the controls, and the moment the bishop and the brothers Gomez y Sanchez were in the elevator, he closed the door and made an express, nonstop trip to the penthouse.

Doña Antoinetta herself waited outside the elevator.

'Your Excellency, you bring great honour to our house.'

'Good afternoon, Doña Antoinetta,' the bishop said. 'You're looking well.'

'For someone with a heavy burden of mortal sin like mine, I can't complain, I suppose,' Doña Antoinetta replied. The bishop winced, barely perceptibly. It was going to be confession time again, that was obvious.

'None of us is perfect, Doña Antoinetta,' the bishop replied. 'As Our Lord himself said, *vis-à-vis* the woman –'

'I know the story,' Doña Antoinetta said, interrupting him. 'I identify with the heroine. Another dove fallen from grace. It gives me the strength to bear my burden.'

'Your message said you had something important to tell me,' the bishop said.

'Oh, and I do!' she said. 'Come into the drawing-room. Might I presume to offer you a glass of sherry?'

'I don't suppose you'd have a drop of something a bit stronger?' the bishop said.

'Give the bishop some sherry,' Doña Antoinetta said. 'After we give him the good news, I'm going to ask him to hear my confession, and I'm sure he'll want to be in full possession of his faculties for that.'

'Sherry will be fine,' the bishop said. 'About six fingers, please, Salvador.'

'Tell me, Bishop,' Doña Antoinetta said, 'how is the cathedral fixed for relics?'

'Relics? You mean holy relics?'

'Of course I mean holy relics.'

'Well, Doña Antoinetta, the truth is we don't have any.'

'Have I got good news for you, then!' she said.

'Oh?'

'I have cast bread upon the waters,' she said.

'You don't say?' the bishop replied, taking a pull at his sherry.

'Blessed Prudence,' Doña Antoinetta said.

'I beg your pardon?'

'I am about to be presented with a holy relic of the Blessed Prudence,' Doña Antoinetta said. 'And I wouldn't, of course, think of keeping it myself. You can have it. Or them. For the cathedral, of course.'

'Would you mind, Doña Antoinetta, starting at the beginning?'

'All right,' she said. 'I have cast bread upon the waters.'

'I got that much,' he said.

'Against, I must say, the miserly advice of three cheap-skate brothers, who were unconcerned with the honour of the name of Gomez y Sanchez.'

'Exactly *how*, Doña Antoinetta, did you cast bread upon the waters?'

'We . . . that is to say, I, in carrying out my responsibilities to the family Gomez y Sanchez, made a small contribution to a worthy cause.'

'I see,' the bishop said. 'You did give some thought, then, to those charities I mentioned to you?'

'Yes, I did, and I decided against them,' Doña Antoinetta said.

'Then I don't quite follow?'

'We — that is to say, I — have established two scholar-ships, the Doctors Pierce and McIntyre Memorial Scholar-ships, at the Ms. Prudence MacDonald Memorial School of Nursing.'

'Forgive me, Doña Antoinetta,' the bishop said, 'but I'm not familiar with the institution.'

'It's in New Orleans, Louisiana,' Doña Antoinetta said. 'Father Huaretto . . . where is Father Huaretto, by the way? Salvador, go get him! . . . Father Huaretto was good enough to make inquiries about the institution for me.'

'New Orleans, you say? They speak French in New Orleans, don't they?'

170

'Some of them do, I understand,' she said. 'But don't let me get off the subject. Father Huaretto checked out the institution for me.'

'May I ask with whom?'

'With His Eminence the Archbishop of New Orleans,' Doña Antoinetta said. 'And with Monsignor Clancy, the chancellor of the archdiocese. And with the Reverend Mother Bernadette of Lourdes, M.D., F.A.C.S., the chief of staff of Gates of Heaven Hospital.'

'Well, the good Father really did a good job, didn't he?' the bishop said.

'The archbishop himself told Father Huaretto that the school is located in an historic old New Orleans landmark, now converted to good works,' Doña Antoinetta said.

'Is that so?'

'And Monsignor Clancy, the chancellor, who is, by the way, well-known to your own beloved, if not too bright, Monsignor Moran, told Father Huaretto that, in a practical sense, the Ms. Prudence MacDonald Memorial School of Nursing is well run by a nun named Reverend Mother Emeritus Margaret. He also said it is in need, dire need, of funds.'

'I see.'

'And finally, Reverend Mother Dr. Bernadette of Lourdes told Father Huaretto that the school operates in conjunction with Gates of Heaven Hospital. Reverend Mother Emeritus Margaret, in fact, despite what must be her very advanced years, still serves, when the need arises, as supernumerary senior operating-room nurse.'

'There's no keeping a good nun down, I know,' the bishop replied.

'What do you want?' Doña Antoinetta suddenly said, addressing a point over the bishop's left shoulder, her voice changing from soft and gentle to firm and furious. 'Who let you in here?'

'Good afternoon, Madame,' a bearded man said. 'My name is John Smith, and I am from the Ajax Television

171

Repair Company. "Satisfaction guaranteed or your money back" is our motto. We got a call that you had trouble with your purples.'

'Show him the TV set, Carlos,' Doña Antoinetta said. 'You can see that I'm talking to the bishop.'

'Do you always bring a tape recorder on your service calls?' Carlos asked as he showed Mr. Smith the TV set.

'It helps me recall my on-the-spot diagnosis of difficulty,' Mr. Smith said.

'As I was saying, bishop,' Doña Antoinetta went on. 'It was, once I had overcome the cheapskate instincts of my brothers, casting bread upon the waters.'

'Well, your generosity to good causes, Doña Antoinetta, is well known.'

'It is the least I can do in expiation of my mortal sins,' she said. 'Which we will get to in just a minute, presuming you don't imbibe too much of that sherry.'

'Doña Antoinetta, what has all this to do with me?'

'Salvador,' Doña Antoinetta said, 'show the bishop the telegrams.'

Salvador took several telegrams from an attaché case and handed them over.

New Orleans, La.

Dona Antoinetta Gomez y Sanchez
Penthouse
The Winter Palace
Miami Beach, Fla.

Have been advised by His Eminence the archbishop and by Reverend Mother Bernadette of Lourdes of your generosity in establishing scholarships in names of Hawkeye and Trapper John. The Ms. Prudence MacDonald Memorial School of Nursing is very grateful. Would you be willing to

172

ACCEPT THANKS IN PERSON FROM MYSELF AND PRUDENCE MACDONALD, AND A GENUINE HOLY RELIC OF BLESSED BROTHER BUCK? PLEASE ADVISE VIA COLLECT WIRE.

MARGARET H. W. WILSON
REVEREND MOTHER EMERITUS, GILIAFCC, INC., AND DIRECTOR AND HOUSE MOTHER, MACDONALD SCHOOL OF NURSING

The bishop read the telegram, and then read it twice more, because it didn't make much sense.

'I don't quite understand this,' he said.

'Neither did we, at first,' Doña Antoinetta said. 'But then we realized that the message had been ... what was that word you used, Juan?'

'Garbled, dear sister,' Juan Gomez y Sanchez said.

'Garbled,' Doña Antoinetta said. 'Something went wrong while it was being transmitted. Look at the signature, for one thing. All those letters mixed up.'

'GILIAFCC, Inc,' the bishop read. 'I see what you mean. And it says "Hawkeye" and "Trapper John." That's obviously a mistake.'

'We finally straightened it out,' Juan said. He handed the bishop a sheet of typewriter paper. 'This is what it was supposed to say.'

HAVE BEEN ADVISED BY HIS EMINENCE ... OF YOUR GENEROSITY IN ESTABLISHING SCHOLARSHIPS IN NAMES OF JOHN FRANCIS XAVIER MCINTYRE AND BENJAMIN F. PIERCE. ... WOULD YOU BE WILLING TO ACCEPT THANKS IN PERSON FROM MYSELF AND A GENUINE HOLY RELIC OF THE BLESSED PRUDENCE MACDONALD? ...

'That does,' the bishop said, 'seem to make much more sense.'

Father Huaretto appeared at that moment.

'Your Excellency,' he said. 'How nice to see you. How was Paris?'

'Don't ask, Father,' the bishop said. 'I understand you've been in touch with the Archdiocese of New Orleans about all this?'

'Yes, sir.'

'And you are, not to put too fine a point on it, satisfied that no one is, so to speak, ripping off our good Doña Antoinetta?'

'I'm satisfied, sir.'

'Tell me, Father, about the Blessed Prudence,' the bishop said.

'Well, Your Excellency,' Father Huaretto said, 'when I spoke with the archbishop, I got the impression that there's been some sort of administrative delay in the Vatican about the Blessed Prudence. The way the archbishop put it, it's still lower case "b" blessed, rather than capital "B," if you follow me.'

'But the archbishop knows the case?'

'The archbishop led me to believe that he had been personally acquainted with the Blessed Prudence,' Father Huaretto said.

'Well, if the archbishop vouches for her, that's good enough for me. We all know how slowly the wheels turn in the Vatican.'

'Read the rest of the file, Your Excellency,' Doña Antoinetta said. 'I'm rather anxious to get through this.'

MIAMI, FLA.
REV. MOTHER EMERITUS MARGARET
DIRECTOR AND HOUSE MOTHER
BLESSED PRUDENCE MACDONALD SCHOOL OF
   NURSING
NEW ORLEANS, LA.

YOUR OFFER RE: HOLY RELIC PRUDENCE MACDONALD GRATEFULLY ACCEPTED. WE WOULD BE HONOURED TO

174

HAVE YOU AS OUR GUEST IN THE WINTER PALACE AT YOUR CONVENIENCE.

> DOÑA ANTOINETTA GOMEZ, Y SANCHEZ, FOR THE
> FAMILY GOMEZ Y SANCHEZ

NEW ORLEANS, LA.

DOÑA ANTOINETTA GOMEZ Y SANCHEZ.
PENTHOUSE
THE WINTER PALACE
MIAMI BEACH, FLA.

FURTHER ON MY TELEGRAM RE: HOLY RELIC. HIS EMINENCE JOHN PATRICK MULCAHY, ARCHBISHOP OF SWENGCHAN, CHINA, PRESENTLY TOURING WORLD WITH DOCTORS PIERCE AND McINTYRE, ADVISES THEY WILL BE IN MIAMI SHORTLY. IN BELIEF YOU MIGHT WISH THEM TO PARTICIPATE IN HOLY RELIC CEREMONY WITH PRUDENCE, HAVE SUGGESTED THEY STAY AT WINTER PALACE. HAVE ALSO DETERMINED THAT GILIAFCC, INC. A CAPELLA CHOIR, SOMETIMES DESCRIBED AS TONE-TWIN OF VATICAN CASTRATI CHOIR, IS AVAILABLE TO PARTICIPATE IN WHATEVER CEREMONIES ARE DECIDED UPON.

> REV. MOTHER EMERITUS
> MARGARET H. W. WILSON

Before the bishop turned to the next telegram, he commented that this wire wasn't as badly garbled as the first.

PRUDHOE BAY, ALASKA

RESERVATIONS CLERK
WINTER PALACE
MIAMI BEACH, FLA.

PLEASE ARRANGE SUITABLE ACCOMMODATIONS FOR COL. JEAN-PIERRE DE LA CHEVAUX, PRESIDENT AND CHAIRMAN OF THE BOARD OF CHEVAUX PETROLEUM CORP.,

INTERNATIONAL, ARRIVING MIAMI 6 P.M. MIAMI TIME
TOMORROW. COL. DE LA CHEVAUX'S PARTY INCLUDES DR.
B. F. PIERCE, DR. J. F. X. MCINTYRE, DR. T. MULLINS
YANCEY, DR. W. K. WALDOWSKI, AND SEVERAL OTHERS.
FLORIDA DIVISION, CHEVAUX PETROLEUM CORP., INTER-
NATIONAL, TALLAHASSEE, WHICH IS TO BE BILLED FOR
ALL SERVICES FURNISHED, HAS BEEN ADVISED AND WILL
ARRANGE FOR GROUND TRANSPORTATION.

> C. CARROL LIPSHUTZ
> MANAGER, ADMINISTRATIVE SERVICES
> CHEVAUX PETROLEUM, ALASKA

'I seem to recall one of those names,' the bishop said. 'The name T. Mullins Yancey somehow rings a bell.'

'We have, of course, ignored that part about billing Chevaux Petroleum Corporation,' Doña Antoinetta said.

'Doctors Pierce and McIntyre, Your Excellency,' Juan GQOMEZ Y Sanchez explained, 'are the physicians who treated little Juan Francisco when he was injured.'

'Dear sister,' Salvador said, 'while I understand why, in the name of maintaining the good name of the family Gomez y Sanchez, we should present complimentary services to Doctors Pierce and McIntyre, I wonder if we're not going too far with regard to Col. de la Chevaux and the other gentlemen. . . .'

'Shut up, you cheapie, you,' Doña Antoinetta said.

The bishop read the next telegram.

WASHINGTON, D.C.
FROM THE ROYAL HUSSIDIC EMBASSY

MANAGER
WINTER PALACE HOTEL
MIAMI BEACH, FLA.

IN THE NAME OF HIS MOST ISLAMIC MAJESTY, MAY HIS
TRIBE INCREASE, YOU ARE COMMANDED TO PROVIDE

SUITABLE ACCOMMODATIONS FOR HIS ROYAL HIGHNESS THE CROWN PRINCE HASSAN AD KAYAM, AMBASSADOR EXTRAORDINARY AND PLENIPOTENTIARY TO THE UNITED STATES, COMMENCING AT APPROXIMATELY 6 P.M. YOUR TIME TOMORROW FOR SUCH TIME AS HIS ROYAL HIGHNESS MAY DEIGN TO HONOUR YOUR HOTEL WITH HIS PRESENCE, HIS ROYAL HIGHNESS' PARTY INCLUDES THE FOLLOWING: HIS EMINENCE, JOHN PATRICK MULCAHY, INFIDEL ARCHBISHOP OF SWENGCHAN; HIS EXCELLENCY EL NOIL SNOIL THE MAGNIFICENT, ROYAL HUSSIDIC AMBASSADOR EXTRAORDINARY AND PLENIPOTENTIARY AT LARGE;* THE BARONESS GENEVIEVE D'IBERVILLE; MADAME ESMERELDA HOFFENBURG, THE BALLERINA.

IT IS HIS ROYAL HIGHNESS' MOST GRACIOUS INTENTION TO HONOUR THE CEREMONIES INVOLVING PRUDENCE MACDONALD, DOCTORS PIERCE AND MCINTYRE, AND THE HOLY RELIC WITH HIS BENEVOLENT PRESENCE. PLEASE SEE TO IT THAT THE FLOOR, OR FLOORS, PROVIDED FOR HIS ROYAL HIGHNESS ARE IN PROXIMITY TO THE ACCOMMODATIONS PROVIDED FOR MEMBERS OF THE OTHER PARTICIPANTS IN THIS INFIDEL RITE.

AHMED MOHAMMAD, SR.
ROYAL HUSSIDIC AMBASSADOR TO THE
UNITED STATES OF AMERICA

'I'm not entirely sure I care for that remark about "infidel rite," ' the bishop said. 'But, on the other hand, we of the true faith must be prepared to make sacrifices in the name of ecumenism. Certainly the archbishop would not be travelling

---

*This was, of course, a reference to Boris Alexandrovich Korsky-Rimsakov, who, when ennobled by the King of Hussid, Hassan's father, had been given the Hussidic name of El Noil Snoil (in French: *Les Lion Boules*) in recognition of his many accomplishments. His appointment as ambassador at large saved the maestro such petty annoyances as going through customs and obeying speeding regulations while travelling.

177

with all these pagans if he didn't hold out some hope for their salvation.'

'My thinking exactly, Bishop,' Doña Antoinetta said. 'And if what they say is true about the wealth of those Arabs, the presence of His Royal Highness in our inn might, so to speak, erase the red ink from the ledger.'

The bishop turned to the next telegram:

BAYOU PERDU, LA.

RESERVATIONS MANAGER
WINTER PALACE HOTEL
MIAMI BEACH, FLA.

PLEASE RESERVE ACCOMMODATIONS FOR THE 48-MEMBER BAYOU PERDU COUNCIL, KNIGHTS OF COLUMBUS, MARCHING BAND, ARRIVING MIAMI APPROXIMATELY 6 P.M. TOMORROW TO PARTICIPATE IN CEREMONIES INVOLVING PRUDENCE MACDONALD AND REVEREND MOTHER HOT LIPS. SUGGEST PROCURING ADEQUATE SUPPLIES OF HAY AND OATS FOR MARCHING BAND'S CEREMONIAL GOATS. GILIAFCC, INC. A CAPELLA CHOIR TRAVELLING WITH US, BUT SUGGEST WIDEST POSSIBLE SEPARATION OF RESPECTIVE ACCOMMODATIONS. KNIGHTS OF COLUMBUS' EXPENSES TO BE BILLED TO ME AS EXALTED DEPUTY GRAND VIZIER OF THE PURSE, C/O FIRST NATIONAL BANK OF NEW ORLEANS, BAYOU PERDU BRANCH, BAYOU PERDU, LA.

FATHER JAQUES DE PRESSEPS
PASTOR, CHURCH OF THE IMMACULATE
CONCEPTION, AND CHAPLAIN, BAYOU
PERDU COUNCIL, K. OF C.

'How nice,' Bishop Patrick Michael O'Grogarty said. 'It always warms the cockles of my heart to have the Knights of Columbus participate in ceremonies like this. They add a

178

certain, oh, I don't know, a certain *je ne sais quoi*, as they say in France.'

The warm smile he flashed at Doña Antoinetta soured suddenly as the bishop recalled what those lousy Frenchmen had done to him just three days before.

CHAPTER SIXTEEN

At almost the exact moment Bishop O'Grogarty had marched with dignity through the HOT door of the Winter Palace, Monsignor John Joseph Clancy had marched, with the firm if reluctant tread of some martyr about to be fed to the lions, into the office of His Eminence, the Archbishop of New Orleans. . . .

His Eminence was in good spirits. He had spent the afternoon in work involving a long walk down stretches of God's green grass. Not only had he, together with Mr. M. (for Moishe) Seymour Goldberg, senior legal counsel to the archdiocese, resolved several pressing legal problems involving the archdiocese, but Moishe had had trouble with his iron shots, and the archbishop had beaten him by six strokes. The archbishop, as the monsignor entered his office, was wearing a broad smile. It might not really be very Christian to laugh at another's misfortunes, but, on the other hand, there had been a certain undeniable element of humour in the sight of a man frequently described as the dean of the New Orleans bar wrapping the shafts of his golf clubs around a sturdy oak in absolute rage.

'Come on in, Jack,' the archbishop said. 'I'm about to take a little something for my digestion.' He took from the lower right-hand drawer of his desk a quart of Leprechaun's Nectar straight Irish whisky and two six-ounce silver goblets.

'None for me, thank you,' Monsignor Clancy replied automatically; then he instantly changed his mind. 'Perhaps,' he said, 'under the circumstances . . .'

'Good for what ails you, Jack,' the archbishop said. Then: 'What circumstances, Jack?'

'I've just had a little chat with Father dePresseps, Your Eminence,' Monsignor Clancy said, taking the sterling silver goblet and tossing its contents down. 'Mud in your eye,' he said.

'Mud in *your* eye,' the archbishop replied. 'And what did you and the good Father talk about, Jack?'

'He's going to Miami, Your Eminence,' the monsignor said. He extended the goblet for a refill. None was forthcoming.

'Oh?' the archbishop said.

'With the Bayou Perdu Council Marching Band,' Monsignor Clancy added.

'Is that so?' the archbishop said. 'Ceremonial goats and all?'

'Yes, sir. Ceremonial goats – and the GILIAFCC, Inc., a cappella choir.'

'You want to tell me how that happened, Jack?' the archbishop asked. 'I thought we'd sort of agreed that putting the Bayou Perdu Council, K. of C., together with anything connected with the GILIAFCC, Inc., was carrying the move toward Christian unity a bit too far, too soon.'

'Well, I didn't know about it, of course,' Monsignor Clancy replied somewhat uneasily. 'I heard about it after the fact.'

'What happened, Jack?'

'Well, Your Eminence, the best I can figure out, what happened is that Hot Lips called the aviation division of Chevaux Petroleum to schedule an airplane. You know how close she is to Horsey, and Horsey left orders that she can have a plane any time she wants one if there's one that's not in use.'

'I've heard,' the archbishop said. 'I know now what "generous to a fault" really means. Reverend Mother Emeritus wants to go where?'

'To Miami,' Monsignor Clancy said.

'Jack, this wouldn't have anything to do with that scholarship those Cubans set up?'

'I'm afraid so, Your Eminence,' Monsignor Clancy replied. 'She and Prudence are going to give the family Gomez y Sanchez one of those little statues.'

'The ones they call "holy relics"?'

'I'm afraid so,' Monsignor Clancy said.

'And how did Father dePresseps become involved?'

'He was at Bayou Perdu International Airport when she called,' Monsignor Clancy reported. 'He was arranging for the annual blessing of the aircraft fleet.'

'And?'

'He was naturally curious, so Hot Lips told him that they were going to Miami.'

'And he didn't try to dissuade her?'

'No, sir. Apparently he doesn't quite understand that there are holy relics and *holy relics*. And since Horsey was going to be involved, and since the plane was going anyway . . .'

'He decided that it would be a nice thing for the marching band, ceremonial goats and all, to participate?'

'Yes, sir.'

'It's too late to stop them?'

'Yes, sir.'

'And you've done nothing *about* this, Jack?' the archbishop said.

'Yes, sir, I tried. I did what I could.'

'Fill me in, Jack.'

'Well, while I hated to bother him, I figured this was sort of an emergency, so I called Archbishop Mulcahy in the Vatican.'

'Good thinking, Jack! What did His Eminence have to say?'

'The Vatican reported that he had been ordered to take a two-week vacation.'

'Who can order an archbishop to take — *he* ordered him to take a vacation, personally?'

'So I was led to believe, Your Eminence.'

'So you couldn't reach the archbishop?'

'No, sir. So I decided to meet the issue head on. I tried to contact Horsey, to get him to cancel the airplane.'

'And?'

'Horsey was in Alaska. With François Mulligan. Your Eminence will remember I told you about that?'

'How could I forget? Well, what happened?'

'Chevaux Petroleum put me through to Prudhoe Bay, on the North Slope, and they told me that Horsey had left a few hours before.'

'Where had he gone?'

'An Air Hussid DC–9 had just picked him and François up.'

'And did you try to contact him aboard the Air Hussid aircraft?'

'Yes, sir, of course. But the Air Hussid radio operator said they were far too busy to take any calls from infidels.'

'That's *all*?'

'I next contacted Dr. Pierce,' Monsignor Clancy said.

'Hawkeye! Good thinking, Jack!'

'I spoke with Mrs. Pierce,' Monsignor Clancy said.

'And you told her the problem?'

'I simply asked her where Hawkeye was,' Monsignor Clancy replied. 'And she volunteered the information that he and Trapper John had just left Spruce Harbour.'

'Oh?'

'On an Air Hussid aircraft.'

'You don't say?'

'The pilot-in-command, Your Eminence,' Monsignor Clancy said, 'is apparently His Eminence the Archbishop of Swengchan!'

'Don't tell me! Let me guess! They're going to Miami?'

'Yes, sir.'

'Anything you've left out?'

'There are two other doctors, or a doctor and a dentist, aboard the airplane.'

'Who might they be?'

'One of them is Walter Waldowski – he's the dentist. The other is a physician named T. Mullins Yancey.'

'T. Mullins Yancey? That name is vaguely familiar,' the archbishop mused. Then, apparently, there was recognition. '*T. Mullins Yancey!* T. MULLINS YANCEY?'

'Yes, sir,' the monsignor said. 'And I'm afraid it's *the* T. Mullins Yancey.'

183

The Archbishop of New Orleans filled both silver goblets to overflowing and handed one to Monsignor Clancy.

'All we need to tie it up with a red, red ribbon,' the archbishop said, 'is to hear that Boris Korsky-Rimsakov is with them.'

'I'm afraid so, Your Eminence,' Monsignor Clancy said. 'And so I thought I'd better bring it to your attention.'

'Thanks a lot, Jack,' the archbishop said. He drained his silver goblet and punched the button of his intercom. 'Get me Bishop O'Grogarty in Miami Beach,' he said. He sat with his eyes closed until the telephone rang.

'Bishop O'Grogarty? This is the archbishop ... well, who are you?' Pause. 'Monsignor Moran, put me through to your bishop!' Pause. 'I don't care where he is. Put me through to him.' Another pause. 'How odd!' he said in an aside to Monsignor Clancy. 'His chancellor said that he was in the Winter Palace. I wonder what that could be?' Another pause. 'Bishop O'Grogarty? This is the Archbishop of New Orleans.' Pause. 'You were just thinking about me? About what? You're with the family Gomez y Sanchez? How nice! No, I'm afraid I won't be able to come over to Miami just now. Yes, I understand that His Eminence the Archbishop of Swengchan will be there. But I tell you what you could do, if you'd be so kind. The minute His Eminence arrives, would you ask him to call me? It's a rather pressing matter, a personal matter, and I'd appreciate it very much. Thank you so much, Bishop. And might I presume to leave you with a word from the Scriptures? "Judge not, lest you be judged." No, no, Bishop. I don't have anything specific in mind. Just a theological truism I have found comes in handy from time to time, and which I thought I'd pass along to you. Nice to talk to you, too, Bishop.'

He replaced the phone in its cradle.

'They're thinking of having the ceremony involving the holy relic in the convention centre,' he said to Monsignor Clancy. 'You know, the place where both Nixon and McGovern were nominated?'

'I know the place, Your Eminence,' the monsignor said.

'When I was a young man, Jack, in the seminary,' the archbishop said, 'I had my dreams. I would be pastor of a nice little church with a parochial school, and I would divide my time among the affairs of the parish. Never in my wildest nightmares did I imagine anything like this.'

'That,' said Bishop O'Grogarty, replacing his telephone handset in its cradle, 'was the Archbishop of New Orleans, calling to express his regret that he just can't tear himself away to come here.'

'What a shame!' Doña Antoinetta said.

'It would have been nice,' Bishop O'Grogarty said, 'to have two archbishops at once.'

'Well, now that that's all over,' Doña Antoinetta said, 'may I suggest that we, you and I, Bishop, go somewhere where you may hear my confession?'

'Of course,' the bishop said, forcing a smile.

'You three!' Doña Antoinetta said. 'Arrange everything to see that our guests are taken care of. They'll be here in just a few hours.'

Then she rose, pressed her hands together in front of her stomach, fingertips touching, and marched with regal piety out of the room. Bishop O'Grogarty followed in her wake.

'Are you still here?' Doña Antoinetta said suddenly, sharply, to Mr. Smith of the Ajax Television Repair Company. Mr. Smith sat on his haunches before an enormous colour television set.

Don Rhotten, America's most beloved young television newscaster, was on the tube, his face a vile purple colour, declaiming in his famous voice.

'There's something wrong with your TV,' Mr. Smith said. 'Don Rhotten's face is all purple, and his Paul Newman blue eyes are all yellow.'

'I thought he always looked like that,' Bishop O'Grogarty said. 'He does in person.'

'You sound surprised,' Doña Antoinetta said to Mr.

Smith. 'I thought you said you came to fix the set because it was broken.'

'I did, I did,' Mr. Smith said hastily. Truth to tell, beneath the beard, he really wasn't Mr. Smith of the Ajax Television Repair Company at all. He was really Birch Beebe, agent in charge of the Miami bureau of the F.B.I., protecting the nation's security by operating in a disguise while he investigated what a *very* senior member of the Senate Committee on Savings and Loans had described as a 'bunch of ungrateful Cubans.' Sneaking into people's houses by saying that you'd come to fix their broken television sets was a standard, prescribed ploy in the operations manual. But the operations manual, Agent Beebe had suddenly realized, said absolutely nothing at all about what one was supposed to do when one found a TV set that actually needed fixing.

'Well, if you can't fix it here,' Doña Antoinetta said, 'get it out of here, and don't bring it back until it does work.'

'Good thinking, good thinking!' Mr. Smith said. He looked at the set and saw with enormous relief that God was really on the side of the righteous. He never could have picked the set up by himself. But it had wheels. He propped his tape recorder* against the wall, turned it on, and then started to push the television out of the room.

'If I might make a suggestion?' Bishop O'Grogarty said.

'Certainly,' Mr. Smith said. 'The Ajax Television Repair Company is always open to suggestion!'

'Would it be a good idea if you unplugged the set?' the bishop asked.

'I was just going to do that,' Mr. Smith said.

It took him, Doña Antoinetta thought, an extraordinarily

---

*The device wasn't really a tape recorder, although it looked like a tape recorder. It was F.B.I. surveillance device 56.904(B), a short-wave transmitter. Surveillees, seeing the device, would naturally turn off what they assumed was a tape recorder, and would never suspect that the device was really a radio broadcasting every sound in the room to a receiver located as much as a mile away. It was, in fact, impossible for surveillees to turn off the transmitter part of the device.

186

long time to unplug the cord and disconnect the antenna. She watched, her hands still held piously in front of her, but with the right eyebrow now raised a full inch above its normal position, as Mr. Smith rolled her colour TV out the door.

When Mr. Smith had finally left, Doña Antoinetta put a chair into a closet, ushered the bishop inside, closed the door except for a small crack, knelt outside, and began her confession.

'How long has it been since you've gone to confession?' the bishop, in his role as confessor, asked. As the bishop, he knew full well that the confessee had gone to confession a week ago; he had worked out a deal with Father Huaretto to relieve him when the strain grew too great.

'A long time, Father,' Doña Antoinetta said. 'It seems like ages, but it must have been last week.'

'I see,' the bishop said.

'That's a tape recorder!' Doña Antoinetta said.

'I beg your pardon?' the bishop asked. There was no reply. He spoke again, this time calling her name. When there was no response this time, he stuck his head out of the closet. Doña Antoinetta, holding a tape recorder in one hand, was going through the Greater Miami Yellow Pages with the other.

'Ah-ha!' she said, glancing at him. 'There *is* no Ajax Television Repair Company. The man is an impostor!'

She picked up the telephone. 'Give me hotel security!' she barked. 'This is Doña Antoinetta,' she said. 'In just a moment or two, a very suspicious-looking bearded man is going to try to steal a television set — *my* television set — by rolling it through the lobby. Stop him, hold him, send for the police, and have him jailed!'

She put the telephone down, nodded her head in satisfaction, and turned back to the makeshift confessional.

'Now, where were we?' she asked. 'Did I get to the part where he pressed his burning lips on mine as he held me to his massive, hairy chest with arms of steel?'

187

'Not quite,' the bishop said. 'As a matter of fact, we had barely begun.'

'Good,' Doña Antoinetta said. 'I certainly don't want to leave anything out.'

FROM F.B.I. MIAMI
TO F.B.I. WASHINGTON

1. DEPUTY AGENT-IN-CHARGE LLEWELLYN FINKLE-STEIN HAS TEMPORARILY ASSUMED COMMAND OF THE MIAMI BUREAU DURING THE TEMPORARY ABSENCE OF BIRCH BEEBE, AGENT IN CHARGE.

2. THIS BUREAU HAS BEEN ADVISED BY THE METRO-POLITAN POLICE FORCE OF GREATER MIAMI THAT IT IS HOLDING BIRCH BEEBE, MALE CAUCASIAN, THIRTY-NINE YEARS OLD, FIVE FEET TEN, 175 POUNDS, OCCUPATION: AGENT IN-CHARGE, MIAMI BUREAU, F.B.I. SUSPECT BEEBE IS CHARGED WITH GRAND THEFT, TELEVISION. FOLLOWING ARRAIGNMENT, BAIL WAS SET AT $25,000 BY JUDGE BAXLEY WILLIAM, WHO SAID SUSPECT HAD 'A CRIMINAL FACE IF I EVER SAW ONE.'

3. PLEASE ADVISE IF THIS OFFICE MAY MAKE BOND FOR SUBJECT BEEBE. A REQUEST TO JUDGE BAXLEY WILLIAM THAT SUSPECT BEEBE BE RELEASED ON HIS OWN RECOG-NISANCE WAS MET WITH LAUGHTER AND DERISION. THE GREATER MIAMI FREE-THE-INNOCENT BAIL BOND COMPANY HAS OFFERED TO GO SUSPECT BEEBE'S BOND AT NO CHARGE, BUT THE UNDERSIGNED FEELS THIS MIGHT POSSIBLY INVOLVE A CONFLICT OF INTEREST, AS THIS OFFICE HAS SUBJECT BAIL BOND AGENCY UNDER INVESTI-GATION FOR FRAUD, COERCION, EXTORTION, AND KID-NAPPING.

4. AN INDIVIDUAL IDENTIFYING HIMSELF AS J. ELLWOOD FISCH, MALE CAUCASIAN, FORTY-ODD YEARS OLD, SIX FEET TALL, 190 POUNDS, LOTS OF TEETH, HAS APPEARED AT THIS OFFICE CLAIMING TO BE UNITED

States senator from California. While fully aware of nuts-and-kooks mentality of California, still find this hard to believe. Fisch says Senator C. C. Cacciatore will vouch for him, and that the F.B.I. had better get this straightened out if it knows what's good for it.

5. Acting Agent-in-Charge Finklestein is maintaining surveillance of suspect known as Doña Antoinetta Gomez y Sanchez begun by Agent-in-Charge Beebe. This agency will shortly forward duplicate of tape recordings to F.B.I. Washington for evaluation. Shipping carton is marked, due to lewd nature of contents, 'For ears of male agents only.'

Llewellyn Finklestein
(Acting) Agent in Charge

The long black Cadillac limousine of Col. Beauregard C. Beaucoupmots, publisher and editor-in-chief of the new Orleans *Picaroon-Statesman*, rolled slowly down Rue Royale in New Orleans, Louisiana. Col. Beaucoupmots himself, his massive, silver-maned head hanging out the window, carefully scanned the streets and what he could see of the interiors of the various watering places that line that historic street.

'Stop!' he suddenly shouted, and the limousine stopped, dislodging Col. Beaucoupmots' plantation-model Panama hat from his silvery locks. He jumped out of the car, put the hat back on, and marched purposefully into Ye Olde Absinthe House.

A young man sat at the bar, a glass in his hand, a tear trickling down his left cheek. He was Lemuel 'Ace' Travers, ace reporter of the *Picaroon-Statesman*.

'Ace, my boy!' the colonel cried. 'What are you doing sitting here in this saloon at half-past two in the afternoon swilling booze when you should be about your journalistic chores?'

Ace Travers raised his eyes and looked at Col. Beaucoupmots, but said nothing.

'Ace, my boy, your commanding officer has asked you a question!' Col. Beaucoupmots said.

Ace Travers told him what he could do with his question. Not only was his suggestion physiologically impossible, it was just a little rude.

'Something is bothering you, my boy,' the colonel said. 'I'm a very good judge of character, and I can tell.'

Ace didn't reply.

'I don't suppose, my boy, that you have any idea where I might find Miss Margaret?'*

'She's in Miami,' Ace replied.

'Miami?' the colonel responded. 'Well, I suppose that explains why she didn't meet me for lunch at Brennan's. I was looking for her when I spotted you in here. What's Miss Margaret doing in Miami?'

'She's there with Prudence,' Ace replied.†

'What are they doing in Miami?' the colonel inquired.

'God only knows, Colonel,' Ace said. 'All I know is that when I went home for a nooner ... that is to say, for lunch ... there was a note from Prudence, Scotch-taped to the refrigerator door, saying that she'd been talking to Hot Lips ...'

'Ace, my boy, I am the most tolerant of employers, but I have warned you and warned you and warned you. The next time you refer to my beloved Miss Margaret as "Hot Lips," you're out of a job!'

Ace told the colonel what he could do with his job.

'In that case, I suppose you can call her "Hot Lips," ' the colonel said, catching the bartender's eye and then saying,

---

*Col. Beaucoupmots, a southern gentleman of the old school, referred to the Rev. Mother Emeritus Margaret Houlihan Wachauf Wilson, R.N., of whom he was deeply enamoured, as 'Miss Margaret.'

†Mrs. Lemuel Travers was the former Ms. Prudence MacDonald. The details of their somewhat unusual courtship and marriage may be found in *M*A*S*H Goes to New Orleans.*

'Bring us four of these, and make them doubles.' He waited until they were delivered. 'What *about* Miss Margaret?'

'The note said that she'd been talking to Hot Lips, and that she'd decided it would be better for our marriage if she went away for a while. She said she had to be alone.'

'She didn't say why?' the colonel asked, draining the second of his double Sazaracs and motioning somewhat imperiously for another round.

Ace shook his head. 'All I know is that she's going to Miami,' Ace said. 'I don't like to think what can happen to my Prudence in Miami, especially if she's with Hot Lips.' He drained *his* Sazarac, his six or seventh.

'My God!' Col. Beaucoupmots said. 'Miss Margaret all alone in Miami! There's nothing in Miami but Yankees and Cubans. And God knows, there's no worse combination on the face of the earth when it comes to taking advantage of innocent females.'

'What are we going to do, Colonel?' Ace asked.

'There is only one thing to do, my boy,' the colonel said, 'and that's to go to Miami and get them. My blood runs cold at the thought of Miss Margaret in the clutches of some depraved Yankee.'

Two minutes later, Col. Beauregard C. Beaucoupmots and Mr. Ace Travers, holding each other up, left Ye Olde Absinthe House and climbed into the back seat of the colonel's limousine.

'I'm relying on you, Luther,' Col. Beaucoupmots said to his faithful chauffeur moments before he slumped unconscious against the soft seats, 'to get Ace and me on the next plane to Miami.'

CHAPTER SEVENTEEN

En route from Spruce Harbour International to Miami International, the pilot-in-command of Air Hussid DC–9 Number Twelve turned over the controls to the co-pilot and went back into the passenger compartment, where he conferred with Dr. Hawkeye Pierce and Dr. Trapper John McIntyre *vis-à-vis* what he called 'a pound of prevention.'

Between them, it was decided that the Archbishop of Swengchan would stay close by the sides of the Baroness d'Iberville and Esmerelda Hoffenburg, the ballerina. Dr. Hawkeye Pierce would, so to speak, escort Boris Alexandrovich Korsky-Rimsakov and HRH Prince Hassan ad Kayam, and Dr. Trapper John McIntyre would stay with Col. Jean-Pierre de la Chevaux. Dr. Walter Waldowski and Dr. T. Mullins Yancey, it was hoped, could take care of François Mulligan.

'That should get us,' His Eminence said, 'into the hotel without a major riot. Once we're in the hotel, we'll have to play it by ear.'

'We forgot Pancho,' Trapper John said.

'He can go with you and Horsey,' the archbishop said.

The best laid plans of mice and men, however – to coin a phrase – sometimes go awry.

When Air Hussid Twelve taxied to a halt at Miami International and the first of the four limousines dispatched by Chevaux Petroleum Florida drove up to the stairway, the first two passengers off the plane were Doctors Walter Waldowski and T. Mullins Yancey.

Dr. Waldowski and Dr. Yancey had passed the flight in pleasant conversation, pinochle, and a bit of tippling. Less tippling, truth to tell, than they would have liked. While Air Hussid took pride in providing for its passengers' every conceivable need, especially when the aircraft was to be in the service of His Royal Highness Prince Hassan ad Kayam, this flight had not run altogether smoothly. In his wildest dreams, and even taking into account every incredible idiosyncracy of his Royal Highness' infidel acquaintances, he had noted the director of in-flight beverage services had not been able to conceive of the demands that might be placed upon the airborne stock of beer by two such dedicated guzzlers as Dr. Yancey and Dr. Waldowski.

The supply of Fenstermacher's Finest Old Pilsener had been severely dented by the end of the Paris–Prudhoe Bay leg of the flight. It had been just about exhausted when Air Hussid Twelve had touched down at Spruce Harbour International, and, due to the brief duration of the stop, there had been no opportunity to replenish the stock.

Two minutes out of Spruce Harbour, when Dr. Yancey, then engaged in a game of chance played with two small, dotted squares of simulated ivory, had called for beer, the steward assigned to serve the gentlemen in cabin four had been — even though mortified down to the tip of his pointed beard — obliged to confess that there was no beer.

'You're kidding,' Dr. Yancey had replied.

'He's got to be kidding,' Dr. Waldowski had added when the steward had shaken his head.

'No beer at *all*?' François Mulligan had asked incredulously. 'What a hell of a way to run an airline!'

The steward had produced a variety of potables in lieu of beer. Doctors Yancey and Waldowski and Mr. Mulligan had tasted Scotch, bourbon, brandy, aquavit, schnapps, gin, crème de menthe, and seven other liquids.

The net result of all this was that they had arrived in Miami feeling not very much pain and a large thirst. They had quickly agreed among themselves that since they had no real role in the upcoming ceremony, and that since there was no telling what liquids would be offered at what threatened to be a religious-type affair, common sense dictated that they abandon their fellow travellers and find some beer.

The moment the door opened, they came rushing down the

stairs and got into the limousine at the head of the line — the one intended, in other words, for Col. de la Chevaux himself.

'Something has come up,' Dr. Yancey said to the somewhat startled driver, who hadn't really expected to have three gentlemen, none of them Col. de la Chevaux, literally fall into the back seat.

'It's something of an emergency,' Dr. Waldowski added.

'Take us someplace where we can get a beer,' Mr. Mulligan said. 'And hurry it up!'

'I'm afraid I can't do that, gentlemen,' the chauffeur said, turning to look over his shoulder at his passengers. He got one look at the look of pained outrage on Mr. Mulligan's face and hastily added, 'I mean I can't do it in under three minutes flat.'

He put the limousine in gear, and it raced away from the airplane.

The Archbishop of Swengchan and Dr. Hawkeye Pierce appeared at the head of the stairs in time to see the limousine race off.

'I wonder where they're going,' the archbishop said.

'If I was in his line of practice,' Dr. Pierce replied, 'I'd make housecalls too.'

'How perceptive of you, Hawkeye,' the archbishop remarked, 'to know that somewhere out there is someone with an aching molar.' He turned and looked into the aircraft. 'Boris,' he said somewhat sharply. 'Put the baroness and Miss Hoffenburg down. The ladies are riding with me.'

Boris did as he was told, pouting just a little. Faces somewhat flushed, eyes sparkling, the Baroness d'Iberville Esmerelda Hoffenburg joined the archbishop. One lady on each arm, the archbishop descended the stairs and entered the second limousine.

'Let's go, Prince Charming,' Hawkeye said to Boris. 'Your pumpkin awaits.'

'You have a most bourgeois sense of propriety, Doctor,' Boris said, 'If I hadn't kissed the ladies good-bye, they would have sulked all day, and you know it.'

Hawkeye took his arm and led him to the limousine waiting in line for them.

'I thought Hot Lips was going to be here,' Boris mused.

'She'll be along,' Hawkeye said.

'Where did Dr. Yancey, the sainted guru of Manhattan, Kansas, go?' Boris asked. 'And why don't we go with him?'

'You don't want to have Dago Red worrying, do you?' Hawkeye said.

'Where's my little Arab?' Boris asked. He looked up at the airplane, rolled down the window, and sought the attention of His Royal Highness Prince Hassan ad Kayam by putting his fingers into his mouth and emitting a piercing whistle. 'Let's go, Hassan!' he shouted. 'How dare you keep me waiting?'

In a moment, His Royal Highness came bouncing down the stairs and got into the limousine.

Finally, Trapper John appeared with Col. de la Chevaux and Monsignor de Malaga y de Villa. They came down the stairs and got into the first limousine. The police escort, a Ford sedan at the head of the line, turned on its blue flashing lights and moved off slowly. It had been decided that while a police escort was certainly in order for someone of the international distinction of His Eminence the Archbishop swengchan, screaming sirens and whooping whoopers would be a bit undignified. The procession looked, as a consequence, like a funeral cortege that had misplaced the vehicle carrying the dear departed.

As the last car passed through the cyclone fence surrounding the airport, the controller in the tower received word from Chevaux Petroleum Sixteen, a 747-type aircraft, that it was thirty minutes from Miami and required landing instructions and a veterinarian.

'Say again all that about a veterinarian.'

'Miami, Chevaux Sixteen. Please have a veterinarian standing by. One of our goats is about to be a mother.'

And in the terminal building itself, an employee of the Winter Palace, in mufti rather than in his authentic personal-serf-to-the-czar uniform, dropped a dime in a telephone slot, dialled the hotel's unlisted number for Señor Salvador Gomez y Sanchez, and informed that gentleman that the archbishop and his party had arrived and were en route to the Winter Palace.

Salvador called Doña Antoinetta in the penthouse, and she came down to the lobby. To her standard ankle-length black dress with wrist-length sleeves she had added, in deference to the archbishop, a lace mantilla over her head. She had also replaced her everyday crucifix with a much larger one reserved for occasions like this.

As the first limousine appeared on the curving drive to the main entrance of the Winter Palace, Doña Antoinetta stepped outside to greet her guests. Salvador, Juan, and Carlos followed her outside and lined up respectfully behind her.

The first limousine stopped. The doorman pulled open the door. Monsignor Pancho de Malaga y de Villa stepped out.

'Archbishop Mulcahy?' Doña Antoinetta asked.

'I'm afraid not,' Pancho replied, gesturing toward the cars following.

Col. de la Chevaux got out of the first limousine. He hitched up his pants and, with remarkable accuracy, got rid of some excess tobacco juice in a conveniently located potted palm.

'Horsey!' a small voice, Spanish-accented, cried, and Juan Francisco Gomez y Sanchez, who had been in the hotel swimming pool when a bellboy had told him about what was going on at the front door and who was consequently wearing nothing but swimming trunks, rushed around his aunt and jumped into Col. de la Chevaux's arms.

The second limousine stopped. An Arab gentleman, in his full robes, stepped out. He couldn't possibly be the archbishop, Doña Antoinetta realized. Archbishops, even Chinese archbishops, didn't go around carrying jewelled daggers.

The Arab gentleman was followed by the largest male human being Doña Antoinetta had ever seen, larger even than the very large male human being who had twenty-five years before crushed her to his hairy chest with arms of steel and pressed his burning lips to hers and subsequently stolen her pearl of great price. (She found this somewhat disappointing, frankly. Giving up one's virtue to the largest, strongest male human being one has ever encountered is not quite the same after he becomes the *second* largest male human being one has ever seen.)

She was so startled by the extraordinary size of this large male human being before her that it took her a moment to take a closer look at him. He was wearing a large, pearl white fedora, the brim up on one side and down on the other. He a full beard. He wore a navy blue cape, fixed at the collar with a golden rope. On his ring finger he wore an enormous diamond ring. Under the cape he wore a black suit and shirt; the collar of the latter was quite hidden by the cape and his full beard. As he emerged from the car, he said, in a voice whose resonance gave her little chills, just one word: 'God!'

Boris Alexandrovich Korsky-Rimsakov had planned to add, 'I'm glad *that* trip is over. I felt like a god-damned sardine in there with you two,' but he had been stilled by a look from Hawkeye.

Now it was his turn to be startled. A large woman, a little long in the tooth but not at all bad-looking, dressed, to judge by the mosquito net around her head, to go to a funeral in a swamp, was advancing on him.

'Your Eminence!' she said, grabbing his hand and attempting to kiss what she thought was a bishop's episcopal ring.

'No autographs,' Boris said, backing up. 'I am here incognito.'

Dr. Pierce now got out of the car. Juan Francisco jumped out of Horsey's arms and ran into Hawkeye's.

'Aunt Antoinetta,' Juan Francisco said, 'this is Dr. Hawkeye!'

'Who is this man?' Doña Antoinetta asked, indicating Boris, who had climbed onto the roof of the limousine.

'If she doesn't know who I am, why does she want to kiss my hand?' Boris asked. 'More important, how come she doesn't recognize the world's greatest opera singer?'

The third limousine glided up, the door opened, and the Archbishop of Swengchan jumped out.

'Get off the roof of that car,' he ordered, 'before I throw you off.'

'Dago Red,' Hawkeye said, deciding to follow the military axiom that when in doubt, act as fast as possible, 'say hello to Juan Francisco. Juan Francisco, say hello to Dago Red.' He threw Juan Francisco, like a basketball, to Dago Red. Dago Red caught him.

'I've heard a good deal about you, young man,' he said.

'And I heard a lot about you, Dago Red!' Juan Francisco replied.

'I think I should tell you, Father — if you really are a priest,' Doña Antoinetta said to Dago Red, 'that an archbishop is due here momentarily.'

Dago Red looked at Hawkeye.

Hawkeye looked at Pancho.

'Madame,' Hawkeye said, 'may I present the Very Reverend Pancho de Malaga y de Villa, private secretary to His Eminence John Patrick Mulcahy?'

'How do you do?' Doña Antoinetta said. 'If you don't mind my saying so, Monsignor, you look very young to be a monsignor.'

'How kind of you to say so,' Pancho said. 'Madame, may I present the Archbishop of Swengchan?'

Dago Red put Juan Francisco back on his feet.

'I've heard of your generosity to the nursing school,' Dago Red said. 'I'm very glad to meet you.'

'If you're an archbishop,' Doña Antoinetta said, clutching her crucifix as if she intended to ward off the devil with it, 'why have they been calling you, you should excuse the expression, "Dago Red"?'

The archbishop looked at the monsignor; the monsignor looked at Hawkeye. Hawkeye looked at Trapper John.

'I can explain that,' Trapper John said, somewhat lamely.

'Who are *you*?' Doña Antoinetta demanded.

'Aunt Antoinetta, this is Dr. Trapper John,' Juan Francisco said.

'If you were so kind to little Juanito as he and my brothers have led me to believe,' Doña Antoinetta said, 'you couldn't possibly be as corrupt as you look. Explain.'

'Among the archbishop's many other accomplishments,' Trapper John said, 'is his ability to speak Gee Eye fluently.'

'Gee Eye?'

'One of the more unusual languages of the Far East,' Hawkeye said. 'Especially in Frozen Chosen.'

'Frozen Chosen?'

'Sometimes known as the Land of the Morning Calm,' Trapper John said.

'And to the United States Army as Korea, Republic of,' Hawkeye added.

'So?' Doña Antoinetta said.

'In Gee Eye,' Trapper John said, ' "Dago Red" means "distinguished clergyman." '

'And His Eminence graciously permits those of us who were privileged to know His Eminence when he was nothing more than a U.S. Army chaplain to continue to call him "Dago Red," ' Hawkeye said.

'As well as some people of unusual goodness and all-around worth that he's met since,' Trapper John said. 'Tell the nice lady that she can call you "Dago Red," too, Dago Red.'

His Eminence looked pained, but quickly realized that there was nothing else to do under the circumstances.

'I would be pleased to have you call me "Dago Red," Doña Antoinetta,' he said.

'Some people,' Doña Antoinetta said, 'are not what they appear to be. Beneath a façade of Christian respectability, behind a veneer of community respect, there sometimes lurks the worst kind of sinner.' Dago Red, Hawkeye, and Trapper John waited for the axe to fall. 'I must respectfully decline the honour of being permitted to call you "Dago Red," Your Eminence.'

'But why?' Dago Red asked.

'Perhaps Your Eminence will be gracious enough, while you are here, to hear my confession,' Doña Antoinetta said. 'That will explain everything.'

The Archbishop of Swengchan smiled, somewhat wanly, at Doña Antoinetta.

And at that moment, a bellboy appeared with a telephone, which he handed to Uncle Salvador Gomez y Sanchez. He listened to what was being said and then spoke.

'Doña Antoinetta,' he said, 'I have just been informed that the aircraft carrying the good Reverend Mother, the holy relics of Blessed Prudence, the choir, the marching band, and the ceremonial goats has just landed.'

'Holy relics of *who?*' Hawkeye asked.

'Ceremonial goats?' Dago Red said.

'There will be a slight delay,' Salvador went on. 'The a cappella choir, I have been informed, and the Knights of Columbus Marching Band are coming right over. But Reverend Mother, I have been told, has been pressed into emergency service assisting a doctor with an unexpected delivery, and will be delayed.'

'Whose unexpected delivery?' Dr. Trapper John McIntyre asked.

'I'm sure we shall learn in good time,' Dago Red said.

'I want to know about the holy relics of Blessed Prudence,' Hawkeye said.

'In the meantime,' Dago Red went on, 'I wonder if we could be shown to our rooms. It was a tiring flight.'

'Forgive me, Your Eminence,' Doña Antoinetta said. 'Brothers, show our guests to their rooms.'

'Monsignor de Malaga y de Villa,' the archbishop said, 'will stay behind to see the band and the choir to their quarters, won't you, Pancho?'

'I see what you mean,' Pancho said.

'And just as soon as that's been done, you will come to see

me, won't you, Pancho?' Dago Red said. 'I have the feeling I'm going to need you.'

'Of course, Your Eminence,' Pancho said.

'Pancho,' Hawkeye said, 'keep an eye out for Dr. T. Mullins Yancey, too, will you?'

'My God,' Boris said, from the roof of the limousine. 'I'd forgotten all about him and the Painless Polack.'

'T. Mullins Yancey?' Doña Antoinetta said. 'The name is familiar.'

'He's a friend of Dr. Pierce's,' Dago Red said. 'I hardly know the gentleman.'

'But he *is* part of the group, Pancho,' Trapper John said. 'If you get my meaning.'

'Just as soon as I see him, I'll see that he joins the group, Doctor,' Pancho said.

'Let's go to our rooms, then,' the archbishop said. 'Boris, get off the roof of that car and go with Hawkeye.' He then took the arms of the Baroness d'Iberville and Esmerelda Hoffenburg and led them through the HOT door of the Winter Palace.

Doña Antoinetta, although her face didn't show it, was more than a little disturbed. Here was an opportunity she hadn't expected. Confessing to an archbishop! And not just *any* archbishop, but a widely travelled one, one who even spoke Gee Eye. She allowed her mind to consider that he really must have heard some astonishing confessions in the mysterious East, and she wondered how hers would compare with them.

Lost in thought, she suddenly found herself standing alone at the entrance of the Winter Palace; all the others had gone inside. She regained control of herself and entered the lobby.

Normally when walking through the lobby she averted her eyes from the newsstand. The racks of the newsstand were filled with literature of the sort that a lady might best avert her eyes from. But now her eyes were drawn to the newsstand; something seemed to attract her eye. And then she

201

saw it. There was a large cardboard display of paperback books. A large yellow-and-red sign announced:

NOW IN PAPERBACK: HIS GREATEST WORK!
T. MULLINS YANCEY'S *TOUR DE FORCE*
375,000 COPIES SOLD IN HARDCOVER
at $12.95
NOW IN PAPERBACK FOR ONLY $4.95!

Doña Antoinetta walked over to the newsstand and looked in the cardboard display carton. There was only one copy of the book left in the bin. There must have been at least two hundred copies of the book, she realized. She picked up the last copy and examined the cover.

NEVER TOO MUCH; NEVER TOO LATE!
Abstinence is Aeger;
Absolute Abstinence is Acataleptic

By Theosophilus Mullins Yancey
M.D., PhD., D.V.M., D.D.

Chief of Staff
The Yancey Foundation Clinic
Manhattan, Kansas

Liberally illustrated with colour photos, drawings, and maps.

Dr. T. Mullins Yancey was obviously the man who'd been mentioned in the telegram, one of the distinguished physicians travelling with Doctors Pierce and McIntyre. Even the bishop had said he was familiar with the name.

And here she was, about to make a fool of herself. A distinguished author and physician would be right here in her own Winter Palace, and she was unfamiliar with his writings.

As a matter of fact, she realized she didn't even know what 'aeger'* or 'acataleptic'† meant. But no matter, she would soon find out; with one notable, memorable exception, she was already an expert on abstinence. And she was a quick reader. By the time Dr. T. Mullins Yancey arrived, she would have read enough of his philosophy to discuss it intelligently with him. There couldn't be all that much to read; after all, it was 'liberally illustrated.'

Doña Antoinetta put the book under her arm, paid the clerk (who looked, for some odd reason, a little surprised at her choice), and marched across the lobby to the elevators.

*Aeger: (adj.) (from Latin *aeger*) Sick.
†Acataleptic: (adj.) (from Latin *acatalepticus*) Incomprehensible.

CHAPTER EIGHTEEN

Senator Christopher Columbus Cacciatore had long held the belief that if God had intended man to fly, he would have given him feathered wings. The truth of the matter was that he was afraid to fly, and flew only in the gravest national emergencies. He had last flown — and the memory still gave him the chills — some four years before in such an emergency. A subversive, pinko newspaper in his hometown had published a story saying that the senator's hometown had no fewer than *seven* of his close relatives on the government payroll. As this outrageous slander (there were only four close relatives; any fool knew that second cousins weren't close relatives) had been published two days before the election, it had been necessary for him to summon an Air Force plane to fly him home. His re-election was clearly in the national interest, and he had done his duty as God had given him the light to see that duty.

At this time, he had solemnly vowed that hell would freeze over before he would risk his skin and run the risk of depriving the country of his services by soaring off again into the wild blue yonder. Like most politicians, he believed what he said at the time he said it, and like most politicians he understood that a reappraisal of the situation might well result in the necessity of amending his position, but he hadn't considered in his wildest dreams (and he had some *wild* dreams) that a circumstance might arise under which he would again climb aboard an aircraft.

But Senator Christopher Columbus Cacciatore was in love, not withstanding the fact that for thirty-one years that had been a Mrs. Cacciatore and that there were seven little Cacciatores at his home and hearth.

He was in love with a woman, moreover, upon whom he had never laid an eye. And Cupid's arrow had skewered him in the mostly unlikely place, geographically (rather than anatomically) speaking: in Listening Room Six of the Audiovisual Centre of the J. Edgar Hoover Memorial Building.

The senator, at first, had reacted to the tapes sent by Miami's (Acting) Agent-in-Charge Finklestein as befitted a man who had been married some thirty-one years and who had seven assorted little Cacciatores at his hearth. He had, in other words, been shocked, mortified, and outraged at what he'd heard.

But then, slowly at first, and then with a sudden swiftness, he had realised that what he had been listening to were not the lewd and lascivious outpourings of an over-sexed Cuban, but were, rather, the cries of a lonely woman for masculine attention and affection.

As she recounted, with amazing recall of detail, her one encounter with someone of the opposite sex, the senator realised that he was the man of her dreams. He had, after all, a massive hairy chest (one of his grandchildren had so cutely said, 'Grandpa's got more hair than a gorilla'), arms of steel, and deep passionate eyes.

'You understand, Senator,' the man from the F.B.I. who had played the tape recordings for him said, 'that we couldn't use these in a court of law. Not only are tape recordings made without the knowledge of the recordee illegal, but the courts, in their constant coddling of the criminal, have frowned upon tape recordings made in the confessional.'

'Shut up, you dummy,' Senator Cacciatore had snapped. 'Don't try to tell Christopher Columbus Cacciatore about the law. I write the law, dummy. What do you think we senators do all the time, anyway?'

It was a rhetorical question, to which no answer was expected and to which none was offered.

'My God — Fisch!' the senator then said.

'I beg your pardon?'

'What's Fisch — Senator Fisch to you, dummy — up to?'

'Well, once we ascertained the senator's identity, Senator,

205

we of course instructed Acting Agent-in-Charge Finklestein to offer all courtesies.'

'What's that mean?'

'Senator Fisch is working with Acting Agent-in-Charge Finklestein in the investigation of this subject,' the F.B.I. man said.

'How dare you call that poor, brave, sweet, and lonely woman a *subject*?'

'I would like to call her what she sounds like,' the F.B.I. man said, 'but we are not allowed to comment upon subjects' sexual proclivities. But don't worry, Senator. We'll get her. If we can't get her for her sexual behaviour – the statute of limitations has obviously run out – we'll sic the Internal Revenue Service on her. We'll avenge the Friendly Sons of Italy, or my name isn't Carlos Michelangelo Nervino, Sr.'

'Tell me, dummy,' Senator Cacciatore said. 'Your mother was maybe German? French? Polish? I find it hard to believe that a one-hundred-percent Italian would wind up eavesdropping on other people's conversations for a living. You're a disgrace to the fair name of Italy.'

And with that, knowing what Fate insisted that he do, Senator Christopher Columbus Cacciatore dashed out of Listening Room Six of the Audiovisual Centre of the J. Edgar Hoover Memorial Building, ran down the broad marble stairs, and leapt into the back seat of the Cadillac limousine provided for his use by the grateful taxpayers.

'Get on the radio telephone,' he instructed his research adviser.* 'Call Andrews Air Force Base and have them warm up the fastest jet in their fleet for a flight to Miami.'

*As a gesture to show that they were not above belt-tightening in the national interest, the Senate had voted unanimously to eliminate chauffeur-driven limousines for all but a few senior senators. Technically, the limousine in which Senator Cacciatore rode about was a 'utility vehicle, general purpose' and the driver of same, who had previously driven the senator's limousine, was on the Federal payroll as a 'research adviser' (GS-12, $22,560 per annum).

'Yes, sir, Senator,' the research adviser said. 'Who's going to Miami?'

'I am, dummy,' the senator replied. 'On the way to Andrews, stop by a florist. I need a dozen long-stemmed roses.'

'Yes, sir, Senator.'

'And you better stop by a liquor store, too,' the senator said. 'I'll need a couple of bottles of champagne for dear Antoinetta ... dear *Tony* ... and I'll need a little something to give me courage to face the flight.'

The senator had one more thought as they raced through Washington traffic.

'Call the office,' he said. 'Have them send a telegram to Senator Fisch, care of the F.B.I. in Miami. The message is, "Whatever you're doing, Fisch, stop it!" '

'Yes, sir, Senator,' the research adviser said.

His Eminence, John Patrick Mulcahy, Archbishop of Swengchan, attired in the formal vestments of his office, examined himself in the mirror. He had dreamed, when he had first decided to take Holy Orders, of bringing the word of God to savages.

His dream and prayers had been answered, in a manner of speaking, he told himself. He had pictured himself sweating in a tropical climate like this one − but the location he'd had in mind had been a hut in Africa or a rude church carved of native teak in the upper reaches of the Amazon, not an air-conditioned penthouse in a hotel called the Winter Palace in Miami Beach, Florida.

He had seen himself, in his mind's eye, in tattered shirt and shorts, only his reversed collar setting him apart from the others in the jungle. Well, no one, His Eminence realised, seeing him as he was dressed now, was liable to mistake him for a white hunter or a timber cutter.

But as far as pagan religions were concerned, His Eminence was convinced that no assembly of African cannibals or Amazonian spirit worshippers could possibly be

harder to bring into the fold than the followers of the God Is
Love in All Forms Christian Church, Inc.

His thoughts were interrupted by a knock at his door.

'Your Eminence?'

'Come on in, Pancho,' the archbishop said. 'And help me
get out of all this.'

'Your Eminence, I have the honour of presenting the
compliments of His Excellency Patrick Michael O'Grogarty,
Bishop of Greater Miami and the Florida Keys,' Monsignor
Pancho de Malaga y de villa said formally.

'Oh?'

'His Excellency begs the privilege of an audience,' Pancho
said.

'Is he out there?'

'Yes, he is, Your Eminence,' Pancho replied.

'Ask him to come in, Pancho,' Dago Red said. 'And get us
some coffee, will you?'

'Yes, Your Eminence.'

Bishop O'Grogarty and Monsignor Robert Moran, his
chancellor, were ushered into the room. The first glimpse
they had of Archbishop Mulcahy was of His Eminence in
full vestments, including the gold-embroidered cappa magna
and shepherd's crook. He did not look, in other words, like
the priest Bishop O'Grogarty had seen outside the Paris
Opera rising to the challenge of a fistfight by shaking his fist
back at his challenger.

'I'm John Mulcahy,' Dago Red said, putting out his hand.
'How do you do?'

'It was very gracious of Your Eminence to interrupt your
busy schedule to receive me,' Bishop O'Grogarty said.

'I wasn't busy at all,' Dago Red said. 'Monsignor de
Malaga y de Villa wanted me to put on my vestments. I don't
wear them very often, and he wanted to be sure they were in
good shape.'

A waiter, attired in the uniform of a colonel of Imperial
Czarist cavalry, rolled a table holding a silver coffee service
into the room.

'That was quick,' Dago Red said, somewhat surprised.

'Doña Antoinetta has assigned us two waiters, a cook, and a valet full time,' Pancho said.

'Send the valet in, then. He can help me out of this stuff,' Dago Red said. 'You won't mind, Bishop O'Grogarty?'

'Of course not, Your Eminence,' O'Grogarty said.

'Shall I pour, Your Eminence?' Pancho asked.

'Please, Pancho, and see if the bishop won't join me in having a little brandy in his coffee.'

'His Eminence,' Pancho explained, 'has had a trying day.'

'Well, what can I do for you?' Dago Red asked, as he began removing his vestments.

'I'm here for several reasons,' O'Grogarty said. 'First, to welcome you, Your Eminence, to Miami.'

'Very kind of you,' Dago Red said.

'Second, I have just received a cablegram from Rome.'

'Oh?'

'I am instructed to remind you, Your Eminence, that you have been ordered to take it easy for a couple of weeks,' Bishop O'Grogarty said. 'And the second part of the message is apparently in code.'

'Oh?'

'I quote,' the bishop said, reading from the cable. ' "And thank you for the beer you sent to the apartment." '

'Oh, that's not in code,' Dago Red said. 'I sent a couple of cases of beer over.'

'Over where?' Bishop O'Grogarty asked without thinking.

'Don't ask,' Dago Red said. 'I don't think he would want it spread around.'

'He, himself?' O'Grogarty asked.

'Between you and me, him, himself,' Dago Red said. 'He's a very good chess player, you know. . . .'

'No, I didn't,' O'Grogarty said.

'Very good,' Dago Red said. 'And he drops by sometimes late in the evening for a couple of games, and when I saw that he liked the beer, I had a couple of cases sent over to his apartment.'

'He, himself, drops by to play chess and drink beer?'

'You sound surprised,' Dago Red said. 'He was once a lowly priest like you and me, Bishop. He's confessed to me more than once that he sometimes wishes he'd never been promoted. He liked being a parish priest.'

'Didn't we all?' Bishop O'Grogarty said. 'Tell me, Your Eminence, if you can – does he know about the holy relics?'

'What holy relics?'

'The holy relics of Blessed Prudence,' Bishop O'Grogarty said.

'Let me have that again,' Dago Red said.

'The holy relics of Blessed Prudence that the Reverend Mother Emeritus Margaret is going to give to Doña Antoinetta for establishing the student nurse scholarships. Doña Antoinetta is, in turn, going to give them to the diocese.'

'Uh-oh,' the archbishop said. 'I was afraid that's what you said. Pancho, see if you can get Hot Lips on the phone, will you?'

'Holy relics of Blessed *Prudence*?' Monsignor de Malaga y de Villa asked incredulously.

'Don't think about it, Pancho,' Dago Red said. 'Just get Hot Lips on the horn.'

'The ceremony is scheduled for half-past five,' Bishop O'Grogarty said. 'In the Grand Ballroom.'

'Oh?' Dago Red said.

The archbishop had been gradually taking off his formal vestments, which had been handed to the valet. Now he was down to his trousers and shirt. The valet handed him a suit jacket and he shrugged into it.

'Your Eminence,' Bishop O'Grogarty said. 'Have we met before?'

'I don't think so,' Dago Red said, sitting down in an armchair, lighting a cigar, and adding just a drop or two more brandy to his coffee. 'Why do you ask?'

'You look familiar somehow,' Bishop O'Grogarty said. 'I'm sure I've seen you somewhere.'

'Well, I was a priest in China, right out of the seminary,' Dago Red said. 'Then I was an army chaplain. Then I went to Rome.'

'I'm probably mistaken,' Bishop O'Grogarty said, 'but I'd swear that I've seen you somewhere before, and not too long ago.'

'Well, there're a lot of Irish priests around,' Dago Red said. 'Probably someone that looked like me.'

A look of sudden shock crossed the face of the Bishop of Greater Miami and the Florida Keys.

'Your Eminence!' he said. 'You wouldn't have been in . . . no, forget it.'

'I beg your pardon?' Dago Red said.

'Your Eminence,' Pancho interrupted. 'That lady you wish to speak to?'*

'What about her?'

'She went swimming, Your Eminence,' Pancho said. 'With another lady whose name has recently come up.'

'She probably wanted to relax before the ceremony,' Dago Red said. He looked at his watch. 'My, it's already four-fifteen. We don't have much time, do we?'

'No, we don't,' Bishop O'Grogarty said. 'We've taken too much of your time, Your Eminence, haven't we?'

'Not at all, but we are running a little short. . . .' Dago Red said. He got out of his chair and eased the bishop and Monsignor Moran out of the room.

'We'll see you at the ceremony,' Bishop O'Grogarty said as he left. 'It's going to be on television, you know. It isn't every day that the diocese gets a holy relic.'

The moment the door was closed, Dago Red pointed to it. 'Go get Hot Lips!' he ordered. 'Get her up here!'

'Couldn't we just send a bellboy after her?'

'Go get her!' the archbishop said firmly.

Three minutes later, Monsignor de Malaga y de Villa

---

*Monsignor Pancho de Malaga y de Villa was absolutely unable to refer to Margaret Houlihan Wachauf Wilson, R.N., Lt. Col., Retired, as 'Reverend Mother'.

walked out of the hotel and toward the swimming pool. The pool was crowded. Perhaps sixty men were clustered around the side of the pool watching the activity around the diving board. Roughly an equal number of women were clustered around the poolside bar, muttering darkly among themselves.

There were two women near the diving board, a small one and a slightly larger one. Both wore bikinis. The larger of the two, who was also somewhat older, walked to the end of the high board. There was applause as she walked out, and louder applause and some cheers and whistling as she spread her arms out. The movement caused her somewhat spectacular bosom to rise even higher and strain against the thin nylon of her bathing dress.

When she bounced up and down on the board, preparatory to diving, the applause and cheers and whistling suddenly died. There was an audible whooshing noise as sixty males inhaled deeply and watched in rapt fascination.

'Shocking and outrageous?' an obviously female voice said.

'Shameless and insulting,' said another female.

The lady finished her bouncing and did a rather well-executed swan dive. She popped up out of the water a moment later, like a cork. The applause was really tumultuous this time, for the inexorable laws of hydrostatic physics had pushed, so to speak, the upper portion of her bathing dress off that which it was intended to cover. As soon as this became apparent to the lady, she flushed, and immediately sank beneath the surface of the water. There was some flailing around as she rearranged her bathing dress under the water, and then she swam, using a smooth breast stroke, to the side of the pool.

There was a little flurry of activity at poolside as the gentlemen watching vied for the privilege of helping the diver from the pool. In their enthusiasm to do the gentlemanly thing, three gentlemen slipped and fell into the pool.

Finally the lady was pulled out, and she stood within a

circle of diving fans. Then the lady saw a familiar face just outside the circle of men around her.

'Pancho!' she said. 'Pancho baby! What a nice surprise!'

'Margaret,' the monsignor said, 'your friend from Rome wants to see you – right now.'

'Why, of course,' she said. 'I have to be getting dressed soon, anyway.'

There were groans at this announcement.

The lady turned to the diving board.

'Prudence,' she called, rather loudly. 'I'll see you in the room, dear. The archbishop sent Pancho here to get me up to his room.'

Waving gaily at the diving enthusiasts, she followed a somewhat red-faced monsignor into the hotel.

Five minutes later, Dr. Hawkeye Pierce and Dr. Trapper John McIntyre were also ushered into the presence of the Archbishop of Swengchan.

'What's up, Dago Red?' Hawkeye asked.

'Hot Lips,' Trapper John said. 'Since I am here personally, rather than professionally, I wish you'd put some clothes on.'

'Thank you, Doctor,' Pancho said.

'Any time,' Trapper John said.

'You wouldn't want to catch a cold, would you, Margaret?' the archbishop said.

'Can I have some of the brandy?' Trapper John asked. 'Or are you going to drink it all yourself?'

'You can have one little snort,' Dago Red said. 'You're going to need all your faculties intact. We have a small problem.'

'I don't see why we just can't go to the lady and tell her there's been a slight misunderstanding,' Hot Lips said.

'You haven't met the lady, have you?'

'Not yet,' Hot Lips said.

'What lady?'

'Doña Antoinetta,' Dago Red said.

'El Stoneface?' Hawkeye said.

213

'The avenging angel?' Trapper John said.

'She is a good, kind, generous Christian lady,' Dago Red said.

'Who thinks she is about to get a holy relic, and has already promised the holy relic to the Diocese of Greater Miami and the Florida Keys.'

'Well, Pancho, you know the arrangement we have with Dago Red. He doesn't make any cracks about the Finest Kind Fish Market and Medical Clinic, and we keep our opinions of the little idiosyncracies of the Vatican to ourselves,' Hawkeye said. 'What's the problem?'

'The problem is that Doña Antoinetta expects to get a *holy relic*,' Dago Red said.

'You said that.'

'She has somehow formed the opinion that she's going to get a relic of the Blessed Prudence,' Dago Red said.

'Blessed who?'

'You heard him,' Pancho said. 'The same Blessed Prudence who is about to be lynched by angry wives at the swimming pool for indecent exposure in the presence of their husbands.'

'What I had in mind, of course,' Hot Lips said, 'was an official holy relic of my late husband, the Blessed Brother Buck.'

'You mean you were actually going to give El Stoneface, the avenging angel, one of those little statues?' Hawkeye asked. He chuckled. 'Buck and the magic dragon?'

'What's wrong with that?' Hot Lips demanded sharply.

'Nothing at all,' Trapper John said. 'Every devout Catholic home needs a small statue of Brother Buck, founder of the God Is Love in All Forms Christian Church, Inc., in the act of slaying a dragon. I have one. I keep it in a place of honour — right next to the Old White Stagg Blended Kentucky Bourbon.'

'I'm sure,' Dago Red said, 'that, under other circumstances, Doña Antoinetta might . . . look differently . . . upon the statue of Margaret's late husband. But as it is, she expects a *bona fide*, Catholic-type holy relic.'

'Perhaps she's been considering changing religions,' Hawkeye said. 'Have you thought of that?'

'Now look, wise guy,' Dago Red said firmly. 'Doña Antoinetta's a good woman, and she acted in good faith.'

'So did Hot Lips,' Trapper John said. 'She didn't offer a Catholic-type holy relic, just a holy relic.'

'I will not stand idly by and see that good woman ridiculed!' Dago Red said.

'What do you plan to do about it?' Hawkeye asked.

'That's why I sent for you two,' Dago Red said. 'It's going to take some people with unfettered imaginations to get us all out of this, and you two have the most unfettered imaginations it has been my misfortune to come across.'

'The thing is, Dago Red,' Hawkeye said, 'that we've been using up our unfettered imaginations at a rather frantic pace.'

'How?' Dago Red asked somewhat sarcastically.

'Keeping Boris separated from Esmerelda and the baroness,' Trapper John said.

'I'd forgotten about that,' Dago Red admitted.

'And patrolling the no-man's-land between the GILIAFCC, Inc., a cappella choir and the Bayou Perdu Council, K. of C., Marching Band,' Hawkeye added.

'I'd forgotten about that, too,' Dago Red admitted.

'And finally,' Trapper John said, 'we have really been letting our unfettered imaginations kick their fetters with regard to the matter of Doctors Waldowski and Yancey and François Mulligan.'

'What are *they* up to?'

'That's what we've been unfetteredly imagining,' Hawkeye said. 'They haven't been seen since they climbed in that car and drove away from the airport. The possibilities are really limitless.'

'All I'm telling you two is that you'd better come up with something,' the archbishop said, glancing at his watch, 'in the next sixty minutes. Or else.'

'That sounds like a threat to me,' Hawkeye said.

CHAPTER NINETEEN

As Dr. Pierce and Dr. McIntyre walked back down the plushly carpeted halls of the Winter Palace to their rooms, the air was rent, as the phrase goes, by screams. First a high-pierced scream, just this side of being shrill enough to be a female scream, and next a somewhat more basso scream.

'If there had been only one scream,' Hawkeye said, 'I would suspect that Boris nicked himself trimming his beard. But there were two screams.'

They pushed open the door to their suite. No one was in the living room, but the sound of the screams was much louder. The two walked out on the balcony.

Boris Alexandrovich Korsky-Rimsakov was standing by the steel railing, leaning slightly over it. He had an ankle in each hand, one wearing a white sock with a little yellow chick embroidered upon it, the other wearing an argyle plaid sock. The bodies attached to the screams were coming from them.

'Look what I've got!' Boris cried.

'Don't drop it, or them,' Hawkeye said. 'It's forty stories straight down.'

'Let's see what you caught, Boris,' Trapper John said. 'What were you using for bait?'

Boris effortlessly raised the two individuals he had been swinging back and forth over the balcony's edge.

'If I didn't know better, I'd swear that was Senator Jaws Fisch,' Hawkeye said. 'But what would a U.S. senator be doing swinging by his ankles from the balcony of my suite?'

'Thank God,' Senator Fisch said, rushing to Hawkeye, dropping to his knees, kissing Hawkeye's hands. 'You recognize me.'

'Is this sneak thief with the outsized choppers a friend of yours, Hawkeye?' Boris asked.

216

'Didn't you hear me say he was a U.S. senator? How could he possibly be a friend of mine? The question is, what is he doing in my room?'

'He said he was trying to protect the country from Cubans,' Boris said.

'What about the other one?'

'My name is Birch Beebe, sirs,' the other one said. 'I'm chief of the F.B.I. in Miami.'

'That's a likely story,' Trapper John said.

'I'll show you my credentials,' Birch Beebe said. He searched fruitlessly through his pockets. 'I know I had credentials when I came in here,' he said. 'I always carry my credentials when I'm conducting an unauthorised search.'

'I came out of the shower, Hawkeye,' Boris said, 'and I caught him searching through your underwear.'

'What were you looking for in my underwear?' Hawkeye asked.

'I can't find my credentials,' Birch Beebe said.

'You must have lost them when this big ape was holding you upside down,' Senator Fisch said. 'Gentlemen, you can take my word for it as a U.S. senator that this gentleman is what he says he is.'

'You've got to be kidding,' Trapper John said.

'I wouldn't believe a U.S. senator if he told me my name was Pierce,' Hawkeye said.

'And what *is* your name, sir?' Agent Beebe inquired.

'Pierce.'

'Well, Mr. Pierce,' Senator Fisch said, 'I see that we're going to have to take you into our official confidence.'

'Not a chance,' Hawkeye said.

'Your country needs you,' the senator said.

'To do what?'

'We are investigating a Cuban lady suspected of all sorts of un-American activities,' Birch Beebe said.

'Such as?'

'She evicted the Friendly Sons of Italy, for one thing,' the senator said.

217

'And you wouldn't believe what a naughty mind she has,' Beebe said. 'Sex-wise, I mean. You wouldn't think it to look at her. She looks like somebody's young grandmother.'

'If you co-operate with us, we'll let you hear the tapes we have,' Senator Fisch said.

'What tapes?'

'The ones where she tells her priest how she misbehaved,' Beebe said.

'You taped her in the *confessional*?' Trapper John asked.

'Certainly,' Beebe said. 'You can't use them in the courts, of course, but they're sure fun to listen to.'

'Over the side with them, Boris,' Trapper John said. 'See if you can get the one with all the teeth to land on his head.'

'I'm a U.S. senator! Do you realise what you're doing?' Senator Fisch gargled as Boris upended the two intruders once again and carried them to the railing.

'Two birds with one stone?' Trapper John inquired. 'Bums away, Boris!'

'Wait a minute,' Hawkeye said suddenly.

'There is a time and a place for mercy,' Trapper John said. 'But this isn't it.'

'I think these gentlemen may be able to help us with *our* problem,' Hawkeye said. 'Put them down, Boris, but don't turn them loose.'

There were other people in the Winter Palace, of course, who were known in the quaint cant of the hotel game as 'guests'.* While the Winter Palace, like all good Miami Beach hotels, offered a variety of things to do, from bathing in the Atlantic from the Winter Palace's private beach (three hundred feet long and twenty-six feet wide at low tide, this

---

*Guests are defined as 'those entertained and/or housed by friends' by those who take their English seriously, with the implication that the entertainment and/or housing is free of charge (a cot in a windowless closet). Such was not the case in the Winter Palace, where 'economy accommodations' began at $37.50 per diem and soared rapidly upwards from that floor.

'broad strand of sparkling white sand' was the boast of the Winter Palace and the second largest hotel beach in Miami) through bowling, roller skating, Ping-Pong, and finger painting under the professional guidance of an expert imported from the Catskill Mountains of New York, by far the most popular means of passing time for most guests was sitting around the lobby (the men in Bermuda shorts; the women in mink stoles) watching other guests.

More than two-hundred guests had been so engaged in the lobby of the Winter Palace when the first contingent (Dago Red, Boris, Hawkeye, Trapper John, et al.) of the participants in the ceremony of the transfer of the holy relics had arrived.

Most of the guests were of the Jewish persuasion, and thus not too conversant with the finer points and subtle innuendos of holy relics, or the transfer of same. But they all knew, of course, that an archbishop was a high-ranking Catholic of some sort, and since the highest-ranking Catholic of them all was friends with Golda Meir, they were willing to give the ceremony and its participants the benefit of the doubt, especially since the billboard in the lobby said that admission to the transfer ceremony would be free of charge.

There were precious few places in Miami where one could witness a presentation involving a seventy-man (or at least seventy-person) a cappella choir, a fifty-five piece marching band with ceremonial goats, and an archbishop and a Reverend Mother Emeritus free of charge.

Here and there among the guests was scattered an odd Christian, and these were immediately sought out and eagerly interrogated as to the meaning of holy relics; as to where, exactly, an archbishop ranked in the hierarchy; and as to what the theological significance of the ceremonial goats was. With the exception of a Mr. Charles Whaley, a hard-shell Baptist from Louisville, Kentucky, who knew even less about holy relics than his Jewish fellow guests did, the Christians rose nobly to the occasion. Both of these, unfortunately, had been at the grape, and some of the facts they

219

recalled *vis-à-vis* the whole solemn business were the products of their imaginations rather than accurate recall of what they had been told, twenty years before, in Comparative Religion 101.

The end result, however, was that ten minutes after the second contingent (the God Is Love in All Forms Christian Church, Inc., Blessed Brother Buck Memorial A Cappella Choir and the Bayou Perdu Council, Knights of Columbus, Marching Band) had arrived, the harried reservations clerk was telling all comers that he was terribly sorry, but every seat in the Grand Ballroom had been taken.

Finally, in desperation, the outer three rows of tables in the Grand Ballroom were removed, and folding chairs were brought in to seat those dedicated individuals whose threats of violence if no seats were forthcoming could not be dismissed as mere hyperbole.

A two-seater F–104 jet fighter dropped like a bomb from its en-route altitude of forty thousand feet to make its approach to Miami International Airport. It flashed across the Atlantic Ocean, speed brakes out and screaming in the slipstream, dropped its gear, raced across Biscayne Bay, and, touching down on smoking tyres on Miami International's longest runway, popped the drag chute and rolled to a stop.

A black-and-yellow-striped FOLLOW ME truck drove out to meet it. A person dressed in the standard U.S. Air Force off-grey high-altitude flying suit (incorporating the last word in anti-G-forces pressurisation) and wearing headgear not unlike that worn by Neil Armstrong on the moon, climbed somewhat clumsily from the aircraft. Halfway down the little aluminium ladder the person climbed back up, reached inside the cockpit, picked up a half-gallon bottle of La Paisano genuine Neapolitan chianti and a dozen long-stemmed roses, and climbed down again.

He got in the front seat of the FOLLOW ME pickup truck and, with some effort, pulled off the helmet. (It had become stuck on the person's rather prominent ears.)

'Take me to the Winter Palace,' the person said.

'You oughta go easy on the grape, pal,' the driver said. 'It really gets to you at high altitudes. You know I can't take this truck off the field.'

'Why not?' the person asked.

'It's against the law, that's why not,' the driver said.

'Don't you tell Senator Christopher Columbus Cacciatore about the law!' the person retorted.

'O.K., I won't. I'm telling you.'

'*I'm* Senator Cacciatore,' he said.

'You're kidding!'

There is an unfair generalisation made about those of Italian extraction that implies that when they become angry, they always become red in the face, splutter noisily, and wave their hands around. Senator Cacciatore became red in the face, spluttered noisily about the penalties for interfering with the passage of a U.S. senator, and waved his hands around.

'Well,' the driver said. 'You're an angry Italian, all right.'

'And you're a bigot!' the senator said. 'Now take me to the Winter Palace!'

The driver looked up at the F–104. The pilot was holding a crudely lettered sign that said: 'Believe it or not, that's a U.S. senator.'

The driver put the truck in gear and headed for the Winter Palace.

At that very moment, across the field at the civilian passenger terminal, Delta flight 601, one-stop (Pascagoula, Mississippi) service from New Orleans to Miami, rolled up to the gate and opened its doors.

One of its passengers, who had been sleeping rather soundly, was wakened by the somewhat chilling sound of breaking bones and spraining muscles as the other passengers stood in the aisle shoving at one another in the ritual pre-debarkation rite of passage. He looked out the window.

'My God, where am I?' he asked.

221

'We're in Miami, Colonel,' Ace Travers said.

'Miami? What are we doing in Miami? The last thing I remember was catching you boozing it up on my time in Ye Olde Absinthe House. What am I doing in Miami? More important, what are *you* doing in Miami? I recall quite clearly that I fired you.'

'You hired me again, Colonel, on the way to the airport,' Ace replied.

'Why would I do that, you boozer?'

'Because you said we were in this together.'

'In *what* together?'

'Saving Hot Lips and Prudence from the Cubans and Yankees,' Ace said.

'My God! How could I forget something like that? Ace, my boy, your colonel is grateful for your faithful service to your commanding officer in his hour of need.' The colonel stood up, leaned over Ace, and made quite credible barking and growling noises.

The other passengers, who had been completely jamming the aisle, immediately moved back between the rows of seats, some of them climbing over others in their eagerness to get out of the way.

'A little trick from my active-duty days, Ace – learned it from a sheep herder in Greece,' the colonel said as he propelled Ace down the now empty aisle. 'Have I ever spoken to you of my years following the flag?'

'Yes, sir, you have,' Ace said.

'I hope you paid attention,' the colonel said.

They descended the stairs, rushed across the terminal, and got into a taxi. 'Where to?' the driver asked.

'That poses a certain problem,' the colonel said. 'Where are we going, Ace? Where are they?'

'I don't know, Colonel,' Ace confessed. 'Prudence's note didn't say.'

'What's going on in town?' the colonel asked.

'Like what?'

'Like unusual activity,' the colonel pursued.

'There's some kind of cockamamie male soprano choir at the Winter Palace,' the driver said. 'That what you mean?'

'The members of which are, shall we say, rather exquisitely graceful and reek of heavy cologne?' the colonel asked.

'You got it, Jack,' the driver said.

'Thank God, we've found them. Take us wherever you said, and hurry,' the colonel said.

'Nothing personal, buddy,' the driver said. 'Each to his own thing, as I always say. But just between us, I liked it better when your kind wore make-up and dresses. It was less confusing.'

'Stop rambling and get going!' the colonel said. 'And stop at the first liquor store we pass. I need something to cut the dust of the trail.'

Dr. T. Mullins Yancey, standing atop the polished mahogany bar in the Miami Beach, Florida, club-house of the Casimir Pulaski Chapter, Worshipful sons of Warsaw, concluded his little talk titled 'Poles Are Made for Loving, Fact or Fancy?' to the enthusiastic applause of the assembled Worshipful Sons, and accepted their kind offer of another beer on the house.

He climbed down off the bar, drained his beer, and extended the mug for another. He then addressed Dr. Walter Waldowski.

'As soon as you finish arm-wrestling that fellow, Walter, I think we'd best be going. The others will be worried about us.'

'How can we go?' Dr. Waldowski asked reasonably. 'The Frog is out like a light.'

Dr. Waldowski referred to Mr. François Mulligan, who was asleep on the floor, his massive head supported by a gleaming spitoon. Mr. Mulligan, to his surprise (he had entered the Worshipful Sons of Warsaw clubhouse rather reluctantly, despite Dr. Waldowski's assurance that he was a member in good standing of the Hamtramck, Michigan

[Ignace Paderewski], chapter and would be without question welcome here), had met three former comrades-in-arms. They had relived the joys of their youth, when they had been fellow U.S. Marines, from Guantanamo Bay, Cuba, via Manila and Tokyo to Athens, Greece. Then the four of them had climbed onto the bar to sing, from memory, all six verses of the Marine's Hymn, and Mr. Mulligan had been introduced to one of the greater contributions to American culture by its sons of Polish ancestry, the boilermaker.*

Recognizing that the honour of the Knights of Columbus was at stake, François had matched his old comrades-in-arms drink for drink. One by one the others had dropped off, until François — muttering incoherently about some gone-but-not-forgotten love of his youth who, after he had, *honest to God!* asked her to marry him, had stood him up and never showed up at the marriage licence office — stood alone at the bar.

It took two more boilermakers to finally put him out, to send him crashing to the sawdust even as his massive chest heaved with sobs and tears ran down his florid and somewhat hammy cheeks.

Getting him up when the others decided to go was something of a problem, as Dr. Waldowski had suggested it would be. François, you will recall, was nearly as large as Boris. Finally the door was taken off the ladies' powder room, and four Worshipful Sons of Warsaw (who had just entered the clubhouse and were in somewhat better condition than Dr. Waldowski and Dr. Yancey) rolled François onto it. Then all six gentlemen carried it and François outside and put him into the back of a Peerless Polish Pretzel van loaned by still another understanding Worshipful Son.

*There are, of course, boilermakers and boilermakers. However, the true Polish-American boilermaker, served in Miami and Hamtramck, is unique. It consists of a glass containing not less than four ounces of 120-proof imported Polish vodka (made from potatoes) and a larger glass containing not less than sixteen ounces of genuine Polish-American home brew that is still in the process of fermenting.

The van proceeded to the Greater Miami Steam Bath, Massage Parlour & Health Club.* Here Mr. Mulligan was given the GMSB, MP & HC special, normally required only for politicians during national conventions. In a special canvas harness, he was hauled into an erect position and placed in a tiled stall. Streams of alternatively hot and cold water were played upon him with fire hoses until he regained consciousness.

François was then taken to the steam bath, where he baked for fifteen minutes at two hundred degrees Fahrenheit. After this his skin resembled that of a genuine Maine lobster about to be served. Next he was thrown into a swimming pool in the azure waters of which floated hundred-pound lumps of ice.

After he was pulled from the pool, he was laid out on a table in the massage room. While one massager (the practitioners of the art involved thought 'masseur' was a term unfit for honest men) stood at his head, bending his arms in rather incredible directions, another stood at his feet, subjecting his legs to the same sort of abuse. Two more massagers worked on the rest of him, beating, kneading, pummelling, twisting, and punching with large, hard fists.

The GMSB, MP & HC special was the source of the common phrase, 'If it doesn't kill you, it will cure you.' François Mulligan lived. Two hours after entering the GMSB, MP & HC, he was installed in the barbershop of the establishment, drinking a Black Pole† through a straw inserted between the folds of the barber's towel covering his face.

While he'd been undergoing treatment, Mr. Mulligan's

*The Greater Miami Steam Bath, Massage Parlour & Health Club had been in business since 1929. The employees, while naked above the waist, were all large males, and their concept of massage was beating, kneading, and rubbing; they scorned the recently introduced techniques used in some places.

†Black Pole: Three ounces each of coffee liqueur and Polish vodka, a dash of Worcestershire sauce, and the juice of half a lemon served over crushed ice.

clothing (the collar of his shirt had been somewhat soiled while he rested his head in the spitoon, and his suit had been rather fouled by the sawdust on the floor) had been cleaned and pressed.

Finally, the towel was removed from his face. Liberal quantities of after-shave lotion were applied to his cheeks.

'Well, François?' Dr. Yancey solicitously inquired.

'Goddamn, Doc,' François replied. 'I feel like a new man. What'll it be, back to the Worshipful Sons of Warsaw? Or shall we scare up some broads?'

'We are going to the Winter Palace,' Dr. Yancey replied. 'Walter has just been on the telephone. They expect us there. Somehow they got the idea that we were lost.'

CHAPTER TWENTY

Salvador Gomez y Sanchez knocked respectfully, three soft raps of his knuckles, at the bedroom door of his sister, Doña Antoinetta.

'Who is it?' she inquired in her soft voice. She seemed disturbed.

'It is, dear sister, your brother Salvador,' Salvador replied.

'What is it you want?'

'His Excellency, Bishop O'Grogarty, is here.'

'Oh, my God! What does *he* want?'

'He wants to escort you to the Grand Ballroom, sister dear.'

'Oh, my God!'

'Is something wrong, sister dear?'

There was a long pause.

'Get rid of him, Salvador,' Doña Antoinetta said.

'I beg your pardon? It sounded just like you said, "Get rid of him." '

'Get rid of him, Salvador!' she repeated.

'Yes, of course, sister dear,' Salvador said. His not to reason why, he decided. His but to trust in the wisdom of his saintly sister. 'I'll tell him you will join him in the Grand Ballroom.'

'I don't care what you tell him, just get rid of him!' Doña Antoinetta shouted. She sounded just a trifle hysterical.

Salvador Gomez y Sanchez tactfully got rid of Bishop O'Grogarty, telling him that Doña Antoinetta was momentarily overcome by the notion of being close to a *bona fide* holy relic, and that she would join him in just a few moments on the stage of the Grand Ballroom.

Then he ran back to Doña Antoinetta's door and knocked again. There was no answer. He knocked again, and when there was still no answer, he gathered his courage, covered his eyes in case she hadn't quite finished dressing, and stepped inside. When there was no sound, he spread his fingers and peeked through. Then he took his hand from his face and took a good look. There was no doubt about it; Doña Antoinetta was not in the room.

Doña Antoinetta was at that moment getting off the elevator in the other wing of the Winter Palace. She wore a mantilla over her head again, veiling her face, and her long, rather graceful fingers clutched the large crucifix hanging on the gold chain around her neck. She bore a look of penitent determination on her face.

Suddenly, she stopped. The door to the fire-escape stairs burst open, and two men staggered through it, looks of desperation on their faces. Doña Antoinetta slipped into a doorway so she wouldn't be seen.

'Thank God,' the older of the two men said. 'The fortieth floor!'

'I think,' the younger of the two men wheezed, 'that we should have rushed the elevator operator and taken it away from him!'

'Shut up, Ace,' the older one said. 'I'm in command of this operation!'

They staggered down the corridor, breathing heavily from the exertion. Doña Antoinetta knew somehow that they had just run up forty flights of fire-escape stairs; she had no idea why, but the horrible thought quickly occurred to her that they were after the Reverend Mother Emeritus Margaret. She followed them down the corridor as they examined room numbers, getting ever closer to Suite 40-11/40-15, the suite Doña Antoinetta had ordered set aside for the Reverend Mother's use.

'Here it is, by God!' the older one said. 'Forty eleven.'

'Everything's all right, Prudence,' the younger one said. 'Your Ace is here!'

Both men beat on the door. Somewhat weakly, to be sure, because of their condition, but rather noisily.

There was no response.

'We'll have to break it down,' the younger one said.

'We'll put our shoulders together,' the older one said. 'Get ready, get set, smash it down!'

As he'd issued the commands, the two had gone to the wall opposite the door, gotten ready, and then, on the command, rushed at the door, obviously determined to strike it with their shoulders.

Desperate, Doña Antoinetta looked around her. Near her were a fire hose and a fire axe behind a glass window. She beat at the glass with her fist. Nothing happened. She took off her shoe and had at the glass with the heel. The glass shattered. Bells began to ring. She snatched the axe from its holders and rushed to defend the Reverend Mother Emeritus and the holy relic.

She turned in time to see the door open just as the two men reached it. They disappeared inside. Doña Antoinetta, axe raised over her head, rushed after them. She stopped in the doorway.

A young blonde woman, wearing nothing but the most fragile of undergarments, stood, hands on hips, looking down at the men on the floor.

'What's the meaning of this, Ace?' she demanded. 'How dare you show up here when you're falling down drunk?' She looked at the doorway. 'And who's your friend with the axe?'

'Beauregard,' another female voice said, 'you've been a naughty boy again, haven't you? And dragging poor little Ace along with you! Shame on you!'

'Miss Margaret,' the older one said, 'I give you my word of honour as an officer of the Louisiana National Guard that all Ace and I have had to drink in Miami is a couple of eensy-weensy brandies to settle our stomachs.'

'Then what are you doing on the floor? And who's the lady with the axe?'

The second lady who spoke was fully, even spectacularly, dressed. She had on a floor-length gown of purple velvet with long sleeves. There was a cape of similar material around her shoulders; it was lined in flaming red silk. A four-inch-wide

229

golden ribbon hung from her right shoulder and went down through the valley between her more than ample mammary developments to her waist. On it was spelled out REVEREND MOTHER EMERITUS. A golden crucifix, a full nine inches long, hung from her neck, the chain also going down the valley of her bosom. Doña Antoinetta looked more closely and saw that the same legend was spelled out in diamonds and rubies on the crucifix. REVEREND went down the vertical piece, and MOTHER and EMERITUS ran along the members. In her right hand, the lady clutched the age-old symbol of the shepherd of a religious flock, the shepherd's crook.

'Reverend Mother!' Doña Antoinetta said.

'Be with you in just a minute, honey,' the Reverend Mother said. 'As soon as I find out what these two are up to.'

'We have come to save you and Prudence from the Yankees and Cubans,' Col. Beaucoupmots said.

'I can't live without you, Prudence, darling!' Ace said.

'What did he call her?' Doña Antoinetta asked.

'Which brings us to you, honey,' the Reverend Mother said. 'Who are you and what's with the axe?'

'I am Doña Antoinetta Gomez y Sanchez,' Doña Antoinetta said. Her voice did not manifest its usual firmness. 'Reverend Mother, I have to see you.'

'You have problems, honey?' Hot Lips asked.

'Oh, Reverend Mother, do I have problems!'

'I am never too busy to help a sister in trouble,' Hot Lips said. 'You look a little old for that sort of thing, but judge not, as I always say. I'll be right with you.' She turned to Prudence. 'You put some clothes on, Prudence,' she said. 'Beauregard's old, but not that old.'

Prudence shrieked, suddenly aware that she was very nearly naked, and dashed into an adjacent room.

'Let me help you, dear,' Ace said, going after her.

'Don't get any ideas, Beauregard,' Hot Lips said. 'They're married. Close your mouth, get off the floor, and wait on the balcony while I talk to this lady.'

230

'You wouldn't have a little something for my indigestion, would you, Miss Margaret?' the colonel asked.

'Out, out, Beauregard!' the Reverend Mother said. She waited until he had left, then looked thoughtful. 'Out of the mouths of babes,' she said. 'Intellectually speaking.' She went to a liquor cabinet and came out with a bottle of brandy and two snifters.

'Oh, I shouldn't,' Doña Antoinetta said when Hot Lips handed her one of them filled to the brim.

' "Take a little wine for thy stomach's sake and thine other infirmities," as it says in the Good Book,' Hot Lips said.

'Well, Reverend Mother,' Doña Antoinetta said. 'If you put it in that context.' She took the glass and drained it.

'Now, what seems to be the trouble?' Hot Lips said, draining her glass and refilling both.

'I hardly know where to begin,' Doña Antoinetta said. 'May I confide in you?'

'Certainly.'

'I'm almost embarrassed to ask,' Doña Antoinetta said, 'but have you ever heard of a doctor named T. Mullins Yancey?'

'Yes, of course I have. He's a dear friend of mine, as a matter of fact.'

'Reverend Mother, have you ever read anything he's written?'

'I have his complete works, bound in moroccan leather,' the Reverend Mother said. 'They were a Christmas present from Dr. Yancey himself.'

'But have you *read* them?' Doña Antoinetta said. 'Do you know what that man *says* in his books?'

'He was kind enough,' the Reverend Mother said modestly, 'to dedicate his monumental work, *Always Twice on Thursday*, to me. I was very helpful to him, he was kind enough to say, in his basic research.' She looked at Doña Antoinetta. 'I think I'm beginning to see,' she said. 'You've just read your first Yancey book. Is that right?'

'Not only did I read it,' Doña Antoinetta said, 'but I realised that I agreed with him.'

'To thine own self be true,' the Reverend Mother said piously. 'I gather you have specific questions?'

'Do I,' Doña Antoinetta said. 'Do you suppose I could have a little more of that brandy?'

Senator Christopher Columbus Cacciatore had not been as successful as Col. Beaucoupmots and Mr. Travers had been in getting around the hotel security that had been set up to keep the common hordes from getting upstairs to see the Reverend Mother and the holy relic.

The best he'd been able to do was to bribe a waiter and take his place in the kitchen. As he moved through the Grand Ballroom, delivering a tray of jumbo shrimp cocktail fresh from the sparkling ocean waters to the sixteen-seat special banquet table of Mr. Isadore Goldberg and party, he saw Senator Fisch at the head table, looking just a little nervous. He was, understandably, a bit curious about what Senator Fisch was doing up there, but there was nothing he could do about it at the moment. He didn't want to call undue attention to himself, and Mr. Goldberg was rather nastily pointing out that he could balance three of these jumbo shrimp on his thumbnail.

He would just bide his time. Under his waiter's apron, their stems sticking him just a little bit in the belly, were the long-stemmed roses he planned to throw at the feet of Doña Antoinetta. That ought to get her!

He would throw the roses at her feet and cry out his love! He, Christopher Columbus Cacciatore, was the man with the arms of steel and the hairy chest she had been dreaming about all these years!

Dr. Waldowski, Dr. Yancey, and Mr. Mulligan had some trouble getting into the hotel. A reinforced company of Pinkerton's finest had been employed to handle the crowds and to keep all but registered guests out of the Winter Palace.

The problem was phrased rather succinctly by Dr. Waldowski to a Pinkerton's sergeant:

'How can I be a registered guest, you dummy, if I can't get inside to register?'

'What makes you think you can call me a dummy?' the sergeant asked.

'I do,' François Mulligan replied.

'Right this way, gentlemen,' the sergeant replied, after François had set him back down. 'I'm sure there's been a simple misunderstanding that can be cleared up with no trouble at all.'

Uncle Carlos, in charge of the activity in the lobby, cleared the three for access to the Grand Ballroom. They were equipped with the necessary special passes and ushered through back corridors to the stage.

They got there just in time for the crescendo from the Bayou Perdu Council, Knights of Columbus, Marching Band that interrupted the GILIAFCC, Inc., Blessed Brother Buck Memorial A Cappella Choir's rendition of 'Miss You Since You Went Away, Dear' and brought a hushed, expectant stillness over the crowded room.

The Archbishop of Swengchan rose and went to the podium.

'Ladies and gentlemen,' he said. 'We have delayed our little programme because we were waiting for the arrival of the Reverend Mother Emeritus and Doña Antoinetta. But they seem to have been unavoidably delayed. That may be what is known as a blessing in disguise. In any event, we will go right to the address by one of our more unusual political figures. Ladies and gentleman, may I present Senator J. Ellwood Fisch, better known as Jaws, the senator from California?'

The applause was somewhat less than tumultuous. People who had come to hear a marching band and see holy relics and ceremonial goats were not at all interested in what threatened to be a political speech.

The senator, looking a little wan and pale, took his place behind the microphone.

'Archbishop, Bishop, distinguished guests, friends,

neighbours and fellow Radical-Liberals,' he began. 'I am honoured to be among you today.'

(Mixed boos and hisses.)

'When it was brought to my attention by that distinguished physician, Dr. Hawkeye Pierce, and his distinguished fellow physician, Dr. Trapper John McIntyre, co-proprietors of the Finest Kind Fish Market and Medical Clinic of Spruce Harbour Maine . . .'

(Mixed cries and questions from the floor: 'Who? What did he say? Is he drunk?')

'. . . that a certain religious object − I might even say a holy relic − had recently been unearthed, and was about to be given to Doña Antoinetta Gomez y Sanchez and her family . . .'

(Mixed comments from the audience: 'About time! Finally? What the hell is he mumbling about?')

'. . . in appreciation for their generosity to the Ms. Prudence MacDonald Memorial School of Nursing, a thought occurred to me.'

(Mixed comments from the audience: 'I don't believe it. I hope he doesn't take a drink of water.')

'I say, it occurred to me that the family Gomez y Sanchez, who, I learned, were about to give the holy relic to Bishop O'Grogarty for his diocese, were really far more interested in the welfare of the nursing school than in merely donating nothing more than a small piece of stone. . . .'

(Comment from the audience − shouter has Irish brogue: 'Heresy! Heresy!')

(Comment from Bishop O'Grogarty: 'Shut up, O'Hara, and sit down!')

'And so what I have done, ladies and gentlemen and fellow Radical-Liberals, is to purchase that inanimate object from its present owners. The funds have come from my campaign fund. I knew my contributors would like me to spend their money in such a way. The full purchase price, fifty thousand dollars, goes to the nursing school. The object in question will be presented to the Vatican, where it will be placed in their world-famous library. Archbishop Mulcahy informs me that it will make a pair.'

(Desultory applause. Comments: 'Let the fairies sing. Bring on the goats.')

At that moment, all eyes were drawn to the left of the stage. The Reverend Mother Emeritus Margaret and Doña Antoinetta Gomez y Sanchez had finally arrived. The Reverend Mother was in good spirits. She waved at the audience and winked. Doña Antoinetta, however, was somewhat more subdued. She had a Mona Lisa suggestion of a smile on her face. She was clutching a book, Dr. T. Mullins Yancey's latest work, to her bosom. She seemed to be flushed in the face and a little unsteady on her feet.

'Right over here, honey,' the Reverend Mother was heard to say. 'Get a little black coffee in you and you'll be good as new.'

At that point, someone the newspapers later described as a 'crazed waiter' went berserk. He jumped up onto the stage, reached under his apron, and threw something (later discovered to be a bunch of rather badly mangled long-stemmed roses) at Doña Antoinetta.

'I love you!' he cried. 'Here I am, your hairy-chested devil with —'

He got no further. A guest at the head table, a former Marine, Mr. François Mulligan, jumped to his feet, lunged across the table, and grabbed the 'crazed waiter' by the neck. He then threw the 'crazed waiter' into the audience. The distance was later measured at thirty-five feet.

An alert stagehand dropped the curtain instantly, depriving the audience of a view of what happened next.

François Mulligan turned to Doña Antoinetta. 'After what one of you lousy Latin broads once did to me,' he said, 'I don't want nothin' to do with you. I did that because this is Dago Red's party and I didn't want it messed up.'

'François!' the archbishop said.

'Frankie!' Doña Antoinetta said.

'What did you call me? Don't you dare call me that! That

miserable Latin broad who did me dirt called me Frankie!' François replied furiously.

'Frankie,' Doña Antoinetta said. 'Frankie, it's *me*, your little Tony!'

'I'll be goddamned!' François Mulligan said. 'Why the hell didn't you show up at the marriage licence office?'

'Marriage licence office? I was waiting at the church! I waited three days!'

'I waited a *week* at the marriage licence office. I only had a three-day pass, and the MPs came after me.'

'Oh, Frankie!' Doña Antoinetta said. She stood up and rushed toward him, falling (whether from passion or from the brandy she'd shared with the Reverend Mother will never be known) into his arms. François caught her.

'Oh, how I've dreamed of those steely arms,' Doña Antoinetta said.

Bishop O'Grogarty turned to Monsignor Moran. 'Bob, I believe I know that gentleman by reputation.'

Boris Alexandrovich Korsky-Rimsakov walked onto the stage with the Baroness d'Iberville on one arm and Esmerelda Hoffenburg on the other.

'You may raise the curtain,' he announced. 'I am here. The festivities may begin.' He looked at François.

'Get rid of the broad, François, what are you trying to do – embarrass Dago Red?'

François gathered Doña Antoinetta into his arms of steel and ran off the stage with her.

'Bishop O'Grogarty,' Archbishop Mulcahy said. 'Might I suggest that you go along and make sure that this time they get to the church on time?'

'Yes, of course, Your Eminence,' Bishop O'Grogarty said.

'You, Boris,' His Eminence said. 'Start singing!' he motioned to the stagehand to raise the curtain, and the festivities resumed.

More humour from Sphere Books

THE GOON SHOW SCRIPTS
Spike Milligan

'Eccles and Bluebottle verbatim, Henry and
Minnie unscrambled, Moriarty and Grytpype-
Thynne *au clair* – an absolute must for
anybody with a funny-bone in the head. Nine
specimens of the most contagious verbal
slapstick ever to assail the ear, elegantly
printed and idiotically embellished with graffiti
by Milligan, Peter Sellers and Harry
Secombe.'

Sunday Times

0 7221 6074 7   95p

AND

MORE GOON SHOW SCRIPTS
Spike Milligan

In this second collection of scripts, Spike
Milligan has made his selection from the
shows broadcast between December 1958 and
February 1959. He has included such
legendary performances as 'Ned's Atomic
Dustbin', 'Battle of Spionkop', 'The Tay
Bridge Disaster' and 'The Gold-Plate
Robbery'.

With a foreword by H.R.H. The Prince of
Wales.

0 7221 6075 5   95p

THE GROUCHO LETTERS
Groucho Marx

'I don't care to belong to any social organization that will accept me as a member.' The letters of the world's only Groucho Marx are now kept in the Library of Congress. With this book, all Groucho lovers can have their own copies of the letters he wrote over the years to everyone from the President of the U.S. to his daughter's boyfriend – not to mention the replies received from such great comics as James Thurber and S. J. Perelman.

0 7221 58580   75p

MY FAVOURITE INTERVALS
Victor Borge

Lives of the musical giants and other facts you didn't know you'd missed! Beethoven in jail? Strauss picketed by his second wife? Mozart writing operas in between billiard shots? Victor Borge has picked all the pieces of the lives of the great composers and put them back together in these unexpurgated, hilarious, sometimes shocking accounts of geniuses at work, play and mischief.

0 7221 17809   85p